Heather Buttivant is a writer and educator who specialises in introducing people to the mysterious wildlife beneath the Cornish waves. Her popular blog, Cornish Rock Pools, won the BBC Wildlife Magazine Blog of the Year Award in 2017 and she has appeared on BBC *Countryfile*. Her career has included working for Friends of the Earth and the Open University and she is a Fellow of the Higher Education Academy. She has Masters degrees in Professional Writing and Environmental Policy, a tracksuit full of swimming badges and an 'I love sea slugs' t-shirt. When she isn't crawling through seaweed wearing waders or running children's events for Cornwall Wildlife Trust, Heather likes to hide away and write. *cornishrockpools.com*

Heather Buttivant

Rock Pool

Extraordinary Encounters Between the Tides

Those who dwell, as scientists or laymen, among the beauties and mysteries of the earth are never alone or weary of life.

Rachel Carson

Contents

PART ONE

LIFE AT THE EXTREME
The Upper Intertidal Zone

PART TWO

ROCK POOL SPECIALISTS
The Middle Intertidal Zone

PART THREE

GATEWAY TO THE DEEP
The Lower Intertidal Zone

EPILOGUE

Feeding the Addiction 272

Glimpsing the Underwater World

Une fois qu'elle vous a ensorcelé, la mer vous tient pour toujours dans son filet à merveilles.

The sea, once it casts its spell, holds you in its net of wonder for ever.

Jaques-Yves Cousteau

Borders are places of contrasting extremes, places where the rules suddenly change and the unfamiliar beckons. Beaches mark one of the most extreme frontiers on our planet, the line between land and sea, where our everyday experience gives way to an alien world in which we are not equipped to survive. On the other side of the tideline, life is tough. There are extreme temperatures, salinity, pressure and currents to contend with: challenges that are exacerbated by fierce competition for survival among the inhabitants of the shore.

The marine world is largely an unexplored one. It is easier to trek to the Poles or to scale the highest peaks than it is to wander the deepest seabeds. Even our shallowest waters are mostly known only to divers. Yet twice each day, for a few short hours, the sea's protective cover slips away. The border moves back and allows us to walk into this curious realm, where every creature has a remarkable story to tell, from the common limpet to the curled octopus. What we know is astounding, and there is much still to be discovered.

With every step I take down the beach, I am heading further into the seabed. I am trespassing in the marine world. More than once I have forgotten my place, becoming entranced by my exploration of distant rocks and kelp beds, finally looking up to realise that the water level has changed, that a current is flowing through gaps in the rock and that my way back to shore will soon be flooded. Heart pounding, feet flailing on seaweeds and slipping on rocks, I scramble to beat the flooding tide, hurrying to reach dry land before the sea cuts me off.

Afterwards, I tell myself that my panic was irrational, that there was no need to rush, but it is a fear I cannot overcome. Even on the calmest day the sea's power is immense, and I cannot shake the knowledge that this world is not mine. Neither can I shake the fascination it holds.

There is a beach that never fails to make me happy. It isn't in the Cornwall tourist brochures and you can't book in to a hotel there. There are no cafés, not even a road, but that is its charm. To visit Porth Mear, on the wild north coast near the stone stacks of Bedruthan Steps, is to take a flight from the highest, springy-turfed cliff tops to the hidden depths of the ocean.

I first knew it was a special beach when I was at primary school and a friend told me that his uncle had caught a giant goby there. Or he might have said guppy; we didn't know much about fish then. Either way, it was a magical creature, with Mick Jagger lips and piggy eyes, and his uncle had scooped it from a pool so deep you could swim there if you dared.

Porth Mear was walkable from my home in Mawgan Porth with a bit of determination and a *Star Wars* flask of pink milkshake to keep me going, but it was easier if I could persuade my parents to take the car to the valley head and park alongside the Cornish hedge next to the wheat field. Every gap in the stacked and herring-boned slates sprouted with soft greenery, festooned with alexanders, cornflowers or valerian, depending on the season.

Beside the lonely whitewashed farmhouse that seemed to belong in a *Famous Five* mystery, a slate stile built into the wall crossed to the fields. The gate beside the stile was always unlocked, but I never went through it. Every time, I climbed that stile to secure the first unbroken view of the sea through the plunging sides of the valley, my lungs expanding to take in the Atlantic air. A splash of deep blue framed by towering cliffs rose to meet me as I descended, past the herd of warm-breathed brown cows to the tall marsh reeds below, then across the footbridge to the open beach.

Between me and the sea lay rocks, and between the rocks lay pools of clear water lined with seaweeds of every shape and colour: greens, pinks, browns and even blues. Within these pools anything was possible. During my first childhood visits, most of the wildlife was glimpsed for an instant and lost to view just as quickly. Fish zipped away and crabs tucked themselves under stones, fleeing my eager footsteps and splashing boots, but those moments, so brief they seemed imagined, never failed to thrill. As I grew, I learned to move more slowly and watch more closely, but the flash of a fish's flank reflecting the sun as it swims away still quickens my heart.

In an ever-changing world, the beach is a constant. It is a paradox, changing with every tide, every season, every storm, yet always the same. It is like an old friend, every part of it reassuring and familiar, but still able to surprise me. Over the years and decades I have often returned to this beach, and every time I uncover something new.

The ocean does not give up its secrets easily. This is part of its charm. The best pools are those most rarely uncovered by the tide, those that appear only when the moon is new or full and aligned with the sun to exert maximum gravitational pull on the seas.

I have never found a giant goby (or indeed a guppy) at Porth Mear. You rarely find what you set out to look for in the rock pools, but I have caught my breath as the shells around me come alive, with strange hermit crabs poking out their black and white chequered eyes on stalks; I have crawled under dark rocks to see scarlet and gold cup corals glowing like fires; and I have wavered many times at the edge of a pool so deep it draws me in, wondering what might lurk hidden there.

There are pools that you can only reach when the seas are calm and sleeping. It can take many visits to obtain the right conditions. The sea rarely falls quiet. The waves that pound this shore build up as they travel vast distances and hurl themselves against the rocks. If you set a course west from this bay, you would find nothing but open ocean until you hit Newfoundland.

Porth Mear is lovely on any day, holding you between its rocky ledges and playing out its ever-changing concert of sounds, from the roars and hollow explosions of waves against its caverns and gullies in winter to the gurgling of the stream over rocks and the trill of skylarks in summer. Even on the feeblest neap tide, the shore buzzes and clicks with life. Limpets scour the rocks clean of algae, crabs froth in every dark recess of the rocks, keeping their gills moist, and sea spiders paddle through the seaweed on their delicate limbs.

Nothing, however, is more incredible than when the conditions unite to roll back the edge of the sea and reveal the bed of encrusted rocks and swaying kelp forests beneath. At these times, and for a short while only, you can walk on the seabed as though you are diving without air tanks.

When you enter this world of lobsters lurking in their caves, of bright anemones spreading their tentacles and of a thousand alien creatures living their alien lives right in front of you, it truly feels like you are breathing underwater.

Wherever I go, I seek out beaches. They are woven through my life; the fabric that holds me together, inseparable and steadying. Beaches are a changing constant in a constantly changing world, lingering in my thoughts even when I find myself far from the sea. Every walk through the rock pools, from the tideline to the low water mark, takes me on a journey into the marine world and challenges my understanding of my own world and of myself.

At the inhospitable upper edges of the shore, I witness the extraordinary tenacity of animals struggling to survive; struggles that dwarf whatever petty annoyances I may face in my everyday world. Here, all that counts is the present moment. The change of perspective can be dizzying, as though my reflection has changed into something I recognise better: the curious child I have never quite left behind. When I look closer, everything about seemingly unmoving animals like limpets, barnacles and anemones is mind-bendingly strange. The sole focus of the creatures that live in this extreme habitat is survival: not to be battered by waves, desiccated by the sun or to have their legs bitten off by a fish. Life, in the end, is all that matters.

As I move out to the midshore, I feel increasingly aware that every creature here is perfectly adapted and I am the alien. Even the tiniest blob of jelly is able to cope with being endlessly submerged and exposed, fending off attacks with weapons and bioengineering that make human inventions seem feeble by comparison. Camouflage, armoury, chemistry and cunning abound in every pool.

By the time I reach the lower tidemark, the astounding diversity becomes overwhelming. Nothing here resembles my terrestrial world and I move with cautious fascination among the thick turfs of colourful unmoving sponges, sea mats and sea squirts. It is a place of boundless discovery that calls me back time and again. This is the gateway between the shore and the deep, a place that fills me with a mixture of curiosity and fear. Anything is possible.

PART ONE

LIFE AT THE EXTREME

The Upper Intertidal Zone

Until I slept on a beach, as Cornish teenagers do during a weekend of parties, I hadn't realised how much life there was at the interchange between the terrestrial and the marine worlds. Even as I bedded down in a sleeping bag on the dry sand above the tideline, still wearing my swimmers under a baggy jumper, I could hear the flicking of sandhopper tails against the material of the bag as they launched themselves away. I picked up a mermaid's purse – the horned egg case of an undulate ray – from among some dried seaweed lying beside my elbow and the long, black body of a rove beetle broke through the sand beneath it. In the glow of my torch, a sea slater, the goliath marine equivalent of the woodlouse, ambled towards the debris of the tideline and a group of bats tumbled above my head, picking off flying insects.

The sea came and went, the waning moon struggling to draw in the foaming edges of the waves and, soon giving up, dropping the new tideline well away from my sleeping bag before retreating. Through the night periodic screaming squabbles broke out among the gulls and small, unidentified feet pattered on the sand, moving closer and away, hidden in the deep darkness. Uneasy giggles rippled through the group when creatures came too close, and none of us truly slept. Short bouts of sleep were broken by stargazing and whispered conversations, but by the time the dew settled on our sleeping bags and the dark merged into the grey monochrome shapes of dawn, most of my friends were asleep. Herring gulls strolling the shore slowly took shape, then the dark crows, a magpie and finally something else, grey and low, sniffing at the ground. More of these shadowy forms followed, some standing tall with their ears raised, some skittering down the dunes and defying the stares of the gulls. Rabbits.

Undisturbed by our sleeping forms the rabbits hopped closer. Doing what I couldn't tell, as surely there was no grass for them here. Perhaps they were curious about us.

Soon, daylight transformed the beach, the lifeguards arrived to open their hut for the day, casting us suspicious looks, and the first group of visitors scuffed through the sand, carrying windbreaks and surfboards. In front of them was nothing but a wide, empty beach, with gulls soaring overhead on the morning's thermals. It was as though all the life on the shore had been no more than a magic midsummer's dream, fallen still with the dawn.

The zones of a beach are fluid and hard to define, but we can consider the upper shore to be the area from the highest tideline to parts of the beach that are only just reached by the smallest neap tides. At this upper limit of the beach there are many terrestrial visitors. Toads sometimes spawn in pools and rivers that straddle the border, adders may bask in the morning sun on the rocks. It's not unknown at night for hedgehogs to snuffle past. Otters travel through, moving seamlessly between fresh and saltwater.

There are terrestrial plants, lichens and animals that specialise in surviving on cliffs, in dunes and at the margins of the sea, able to tolerate the storms, salt and spray, but, except for a few invertebrates that have found ways to hide in air pockets in the midshore rocks, these terrestrial life forms don't survive below the tideline.

Most marine life, of course, needs to be underwater to breathe and survive, but the upper shore is only covered by the sea for a short time each day. Creatures that live here are exposed to storms and frosts, and to the harsh rays of the sun together with drying winds, which evaporate the water and send the salt content of pools sky high. There is an inflow of fresh water from streams and rain which does the opposite, lowering the salinity. Despite the extreme conditions, not everything perishes here. Some species have made this zone their home. In return for their incredible survival skills, they enjoy limited competition and keep themselves largely out of reach of marine predators. They have found ways to cope with the varying temperatures and salinity and, above all, to avoid the greatest enemy of any marine creature: drying out.

CHAPTER 1

Limpet

Limpets are so abundant that I unthinkingly overlook them. Their shells litter the tideline, rolling and clattering underfoot on my way to the rock pools. I barely take a few steps down the shore before their upturned cones appear, living on the rocks. There's certainly no skill in finding them, sitting motionless, only slightly camouflaged by their pale yellow, orange and brown streaks. Their sloping roofs are as familiar and safe as houses, as solid as if they were part of the rock itself. They're hiding in plain sight because few creatures take an interest in them. They seem unremarkable. This is the shore, though, and nothing is unremarkable.

Though it can be peaceful, a beach is never quiet. As well as the ever-present rumble and roar of sea and wind, there are trickling streams, the trills and screams of seabirds and odd booms and gasps of air as the waves force water into hidden holes in the rocks. I'm crouching to examine barnacles when I hear something new, a sound which is so like footsteps on pebbles that I look around. No one is near.

It's one of those days when the drizzle blows in with the mist and soaks you in minutes, the sort of day that keeps the shore creatures active even after the tide has slipped away. Long fronds of bladderwrack hang as heavy, brown fringes over the sides of the rocks, still bubbling with sea water that drips into the flow retreating down the shore. The crackling sound comes and goes, seemingly from all around me, making it hard to home in on the source.

I lift back the seaweed and two large limpets twist back and forth in front of my nose, lifting up the hems of their shells and swinging them round like twirling skirts, back and forth, dancing their way home. I hear the sound again, sharp and grating, like rock being chipped away. That's exactly what it is. These limpets are moulding the rocks to their shells. Only by achieving a perfect fit can they clamp onto the rock and avoid gaps which would let air in and dry them out. Using their powerful foot, limpets swing their shells against the stone beneath them, grinding a groove to sink into. Ordinarily they would do this as soon as the sea retreated, but today the saturated air and rocks have given them extra grazing time and they are only just rolling home.

Limpets are a type of marine snail from a large class of molluscs known as the gastropods: the word literally means stomach-foot. It may sound like a playground insult, but it is a reasonable description of how these animals move about. Although the underside of a limpet's shell is filled with a round muscular foot, its body remains largely hidden most of the time, even when it is feeding.

Gastropods feed using a tongue-like organ called a radula. In the limpet, the radula is fringed with teeth made of the strongest biological material known to science, goethite. When limpets feed, they rasp away at the rock with their radula, cleaning it of microalgae, chipping away at the substrata in the

Limpet feeding tracks on a rock. *Charlotte Cumming*

process. At night, when the drying sun has set, if you put your ear in close to the rocks you can hear the crackles of limpets feeding. At every opportunity they are to be heard noisily carving out their place in the world.

There's something heroic about the ways in which limpets mould their environment to their needs. Between the shells of living limpets, the oval grooves of previous residents are visible as permanent scars in the rocks. Zigzag markings left by grazing limpets can be extensive, almost artistic, especially on slate.

The rocks at the frontier of the upper shore are the marine equivalent of the savannah. Above them lie the desert sands around the tideline, below them the seaweed grows into thick tangled forests. Huge numbers of limpets can live on these plains, herds of them moving out to graze every time the tide rolls in. It's a perilous existence where timing is everything. Despite their dizzying feeding patterns, limpets cannot afford to dither on their way home. They must make it back to their home scar when the tide retreats or find some other suitable place to settle, else they risk desiccation.

Like many other animals on the shore, limpets have deployed a chemical solution. In this case, mucus. By leaving chemical signals in their mucus, limpets can follow the trail back to their home spot. Not only that, but their mucus also has special sticky properties, which make it easier for certain types of algae on which they feed to grip the rock and settle.

In the absence of grazing limpets, the rocks would be covered in algae and even more slippery than they already are. When the *Sea Empress* oil tanker ran aground in 1996, spilling tens of thousands of tonnes of crude oil into the sea near Milford Haven in Pembrokeshire, over half the limpets were wiped out on many local beaches. This resulted in a dramatic bloom of gutweed, a green seaweed, around six weeks later. Laver, a brown seaweed that forms thin tar-like sheets on the rocks and is best known for its use in making laver bread, was next to establish itself. Then, as the beach recovered, it became entirely coated in bladderwrack. It took a couple of years for the limpet population to re-establish on the shore and several more before an equilibrium was reached between the limpet and seaweed populations, during which numbers of both fluctuated. Unassuming as they seem, limpets are an essential part of the rocky shore ecosystem.

There's a limpet I often admire. It lives halfway up the harbour wall in the mouth of the Looe estuary in Cornwall. Boats lift and drop alongside it, egrets stalk the muddy river bed below it on spreading yellow feet, jabbing at sand eels as they go, and tourists lean on the railings to admire the fishing boats. I stand alongside them looking down the wall as the sea flows in, covering my limpet.

There aren't many limpets here. The merging freshwater of the river and salt water from the sea make the salinity highly variable. It's on the edge of what even a limpet can tolerate. Yet this limpet is huge. It would dwarf the limpets on exposed beaches and is wider than anything I've seen on even the most sheltered shores. I've never attempted to climb down and measure it, but it looks bigger than the maximum of six centimetres in length that all my books suggest it should be. I'm guessing it hasn't read the books.

Most striking of all is its profile. Limpets on exposed rocks and on the lower shore tend not to be tall, presumably to help them to survive storms and currents and because competition for food is greater, but other factors such as tidal range and temperature are thought to affect their growth. This limpet seems to have found the perfect sheltered conditions. It's the only limpet on this section of the wall and its sides and spire appear to extend further out every time I see it, as though challenging the moored boats to try knocking it off. Despite the danger of desiccation this high above the low tide mark, there's an abundance of algae about and the shelter of the seaweed enables the limpet to hoover up the microalgae from the tall harbour wall. At this point in the estuary there aren't many barnacles, which can cover the rocks with their sharp tests, reducing the area available for grazing and creating uncomfortable obstacles for limpets to negotiate.

Unlike its smaller counterparts on the exposed rocks of wave-swept beaches, this towering limpet has a low life expectancy. It's already at least a couple of years old, so it may only have three to four years left to live. Slower growing limpets may live to 15 or 16 years old. Every time I pass the harbour wall I stop to check if my limpet is still there. It seems to be thriving now, but who knows if it can survive the next winter.

The alien existence of rock pool wildlife goes far beyond the ability to breathe underwater and cling on through the storms.

Everything about their way of life is surprising and reproduction is no exception.

It's not easy to tell by looking at a limpet what sex it is, but I suspect my enormous limpet is a female. Limpets prefer not to get involved with one another directly, releasing eggs and sperm out into the sea at a coordinated moment, probably during storms. The baby limpet spat settles on the rock after a few weeks developing in the plankton and remains sexually immature for around the first nine months of its life. These young limpets are relatively flat and are often marked with strong ridges and colours. As they grow, all young limpets become male. However, after two to three years as a male, they change sex, becoming female.

Although growth rates vary between shores, and between areas of greater or lesser exposure to waves, only the larger limpets on a given shore are likely to be female. This kind of gender fluidity is not uncommon in the marine world and seems to be a successful reproductive strategy as limpets are one of the most common and widespread animals on the shore.

The larger limpets have an advantage when it comes to fending off certain predators. Starfish love to feed on molluscs and use the many tube feet under their arms to seek out their prey. When a limpet feels a starfish encroaching onto its shell, investigating it as a potential meal, it will extend its body upwards, raising its shell before using the hard edge like an axe to strike the starfish's arm, chopping down then twisting and rasping away to inflict maximum damage. This surprisingly speedy manoeuvre was captured in the BBC's documentary *The Secret Life of Rock Pools* in which the presenter, Richard Fortey, likened the limpet to an 'animated mushroom'.

Almost wherever you go, from the top of the shore to the edge of the sea, there will be limpets of some kind. On most rocky shores the classic cone-shaped common limpet, *Patella vulgata*, dominates, especially on this top stretch of shore. On fronds of kelp washed in by the tide, rows of blue-rayed limpets sparkle, their flecked turquoise bands catching the light in a way no camera can properly capture. Dig in among the tangled holdfasts of the kelp and you find older blue-rayed limpets wedged among sponges and barnacles. Several species of limpet live lower down on the shore than the common limpet.

When they die, the shells of all these limpets are tumbled through the waves and often end up on the strandline, among clumps of dislodged seaweed and other tideline treasures like cuttlefish bones and stranded jellyfish. Some are whole, while others are missing their tops where they have been pecked through by hungry oystercatchers, then worn into smooth rings by the waves.

My own journey into the rockpools began here on the tideline, as most children's journeys do, picking up shells, collecting and hoarding them in a cupboard in my bedroom until the door would no longer shut. No matter how often my parents told me I had enough shells already, I couldn't help myself. There was always a reason that I couldn't let a new find go. This latest shell was always the largest, the shiniest, the one with the most striking pattern or the quirkiest shape. I had to have it and the fact that my pockets and bedroom were full of sand never struck me as a problem.

A trip to Sussex to visit family friends at the height of my collecting phase introduced me to the slipper limpet. The shells of slipper limpets are so similar to limpet shells that they were originally placed in the Patellidae (limpet) family in 1758 by Carl Linnaeus, the great naturalist who first formalised the naming system. Although these shells were later found to belong to a different group of gastropod molluscs, the name 'limpet' stuck. I was intrigued as I'd never seen one anywhere else and they were unlike any shell I knew, except perhaps for some similarities with the tiny smooth-sided Chinaman's hat shell, which is closely related.

Along some sheltered, muddy coasts in southern England and South Wales, the slipper limpet has taken over the tideline. Great piles of them accumulate on the shingle of the Sussex coast, until they are almost the only species to be found. There were so many on the beach in Worthing that, exciting as they were at first, even I soon tired of collecting them.

From the top, slipper limpets look almost like a mussel shell, oval without a spire like other limpets have. It's when you turn them over that you see how they acquired their common name. A flat white sill runs halfway across the underside of the shell, emerging from the point. If you look at them upside down they resemble a slipper, although the only thing that might wear one is a hermit crab that has failed to find anything better.

Slipper limpets shouldn't be in our waters at all. They were introduced between 1887 and 1890 from the North American Atlantic coast as an accident when people began importing American oysters, and first established in Essex. An earlier population in Liverpool Bay appeared briefly but died out. As a child, I was amazed that so many could congregate in one place. It was only when I was a bit more grown up that I discovered why the slipper limpet is so successful (I'd hoped the clue was in its wonderful scientific name: *Crepidula fornicata*).

Like true limpets, slipper limpets are sequential hermaphrodites, able to be either sex in the course of their lives but not both at the same time. Out at sea, or sometimes on the shore in the right conditions, a young slipper limpet spat will settle on the back of a mature female, attracted by her chemical signals. It grows on her shell and lives there, just as common limpets live in their home scar on the rock. Unlike a limpet, it doesn't have to move to feed, simply filtering algae from the water with its oversized gills. Once attached to another slipper limpet, it will stay put for the rest of the older shell's life.

As the top slipper limpet develops it becomes male and fertilises the female it is sitting on. Over time other slipper limpet spats arrive, settling one on top of the other until they have created a stack, sometimes containing a dozen or more animals. A slipper limpet towards the top of this precarious tower is always male, while the more mature animals below become female. The members of the stack live out their whole lives this way, gradually moving down the pile, as when the female at the base dies the animal above takes her place. Of course, the males near the top of the pile of slipper limpets need to reach a long way to fertilise the females at the bottom. The stack curves as it grows to help minimise the distance between the males and females, but in this species, size is everything.

The Latin word *fornicata* means arched or vaulted, and rather

A slipper limpet stack starting to form.

disappointingly has nothing to do with the animal's sex life. The scientific name refers to the shape of the slipper limpet's shell, but I am not alone in finding *Crepidula fornicata* to be one of the more memorable scientific names.

Once again, my cupboards are bursting with limpet shells of every size and height. This time it's my ten-year-old son who brings them home from every beach trip, his pockets full to bursting, as he has done for the last eight years. We look at the shells together and wonder where each one made its home, what age it was and whether it survived long enough to take a turn at being female. Having the time and freedom to wonder at the world around us is one of the great benefits of home education and has allowed Junior to discover his own passions. The interconnectedness of nature means that one thing always leads to another, and neither of us is ever short of things to learn about.

The more I learn about limpets, the more I notice them, clinging on to life in places where almost no other marine life can thrive. They are the first thing I see as I set out towards the rock pools. They are ever-present, quietly, or sometimes noisily, shaping the rocks to their needs, controlling the seaweeds, reminding me that every animal I encounter here has an unexpected story to tell.

CHAPTER 2

Barnacle

Several times a year, I receive messages about unidentified alien creatures washed up on beaches. The photos show a tangled mass of long rubbery protrusions that look like extended necks. Each one is tipped with a hard, triangular set of plates, resembling a head without eyes or other features. These images often make the news, especially if someone has captured a video showing the animal up-close, with the sides of the head opening and a clawing set of tentacles reaching out, clutching at the air. It's understandable that people think they've discovered a sea monster, especially when the colony is as large as a tree trunk.

I remember the first time I saw these animals, as a child, trailing across the deserted beach after my mother and brother as we went to collect the newspaper on a stormy Sunday morning. The loose sand circling and whipping at our shins was all we could see past our hoods, and we kept our heads bent low to one side in an attempt to keep the blowing sand from our eyes. Deep in thought about whether the newsagents would have the latest *Beano* and which sweets I could buy with the 20p lurking at the bottom of my shell-filled pocket, I almost tripped over the barnacles. A weird bouquet of them sprouted from a small plank of driftwood, the original surface barely visible between the writhing stems. I crouched down in the sand and stared at the head-like parts, which looked unlike any shell I'd ever seen on the beach before, the parts not quite connected, like a badly made jigsaw puzzle, with the black, squidgy body of something visible through the cracks.

Mum told me that these were goose barnacles, creatures that attached to any floating object that had been in the sea a long time, spending their lives drifting around the ocean, eventually being thrown onto the beach by currents and storms. It was impossible to reconcile in my head that these long-necked, moving animals, which unsettled and intrigued me in equal measure, could in any way be related to the benign grey lumps on the rocks that I knew as barnacles. I could have spent all day watching them, but the sand was stinging our faces and I was soon chivvied along. The sight stayed with me for a long time.

It's no wonder that it took centuries for naturalists to understand barnacles and to agree that they are crustaceans.

Stranded goose barnacles attached to a driftwood tree trunk. *Derek Buttivant*

This large group of animals with jointed legs and external shells includes crabs, prawns, lobsters and woodlice. Neither goose barnacles nor the more common acorn barnacles that cover rocks, pier legs and the underside of boats, look anything like other crustaceans.

During mediaeval times, a legend developed. It became so well accepted that it is documented in natural history books throughout the period. Observers of the time saw the shell of the goose barnacle not as a head, but as a body, shaped rather like folded wings. From this body arose a long, curving black neck, muscled and moving like the neck of a wild goose. In true mediaeval style, the logical conclusion was drawn that these strange animals found attached to wood must grow on some sort of tree before falling in the water and hatching into geese.

Towards the end of the twelfth century, clergyman Gerald of Wales, also known as Giraldus Cambrensis, wrote in his book, *The History and Topography of Ireland*: 'There are many birds here that are called barnacles, which nature, acting against her own laws, produces in a wonderful way.'

An illustration in the book shows barnacle geese growing from a tree, hanging head down. Gerald of Wales even claimed to have witnessed geese hanging from a branch.

So strong was the belief that barnacle geese hatched from goose barnacles, that these geese were accepted to be a type of fish rather than wildfowl. This was great news for pious Catholics who could legitimately eat barnacle geese on Fridays when eating meat was prohibited.

Almost three centuries later, in 1597, the botanist and herbalist John Gerard produced the most widely circulated book on plants of the seventeenth century, *Herball, or Generall Historie of Plantes*. For the most part, as you might expect, the 167

Plate from John Gerard's 1597 botany book *Herball* showing how goose barnacles grow into geese.

chapters of the book concern plants. However, towards the end is a remarkable plate entitled, 'Of the Goose tree, Barnacle tree, or the tree bearing Geese', showing three stages of the goose's development. The first illustration shows small goose barnacles on a fresh chunk of greenwood from the barnacle tree, so newly fallen that it still bears a leaf. Next, we see a tangle of larger long-necked goose barnacles on a fragment of driftwood. The third picture shows the final stage in the animal's development, which is, of course, a goose.

The belief that goose barnacles and these geese were the same animal persisted into the eighteenth century and, to this day, we call this type of goose the barnacle goose. Even after the mediaeval myths were debunked, it took many years for scientists to discover what barnacles really were.

At first, the accepted view was that these hard-shelled animals were molluscs, related in some way to sea snails like limpets. When John Vaughan Thomas published an account of the similarities between these animals and other crustaceans in 1830, it was still controversial. Charles Darwin also researched the group a couple of decades later, noting various features of their anatomy and reproduction that demonstrated they were crustaceans. These days, with the aid of modern microscopes and a plankton net, it is now easy for us to see that Vaughan Thomas and Darwin were right.

Like many other marine species, including limpets, barnacles start life in the plankton. This soup of microscopic algae (phytoplankton) and animals (zooplankton) is the base of the marine food chain, feeding everything from tiny coral polyps, to 18-metre-long right whales. Phytoplankton is so abundant that it is estimated to produce at least half of the world's oxygen through photosynthesis. Of course, these microscopic plants need sunlight to make their food and can only survive near the surface of the sea, so many species of zooplankton make an epic migratory journey to the surface waters every single night to feed on phytoplankton, before returning to hide from predators under the cover of deeper, darker waters by day. The term plankton is usually applied to any small species that float and these can be incredibly abundant; a single teaspoon of sea water can contain more than a million individuals. However, the plankton also comprises some larger animals, known as megaplankton, like jellyfish.

Putting a plankton mix under a powerful microscope is a revelation. A seemingly empty Petri dish can be so thick with life that it makes me wonder about all those times I've accidentally swallowed sea water. There are rectangular and oval phytoplankton, plus zooplankton with a huge range of body shapes, from the curled to the long to the spiky. Antennae stick out in all directions and transparent tentacles feel their way. Many have see-through bodies with mysterious, pulsing innards, but there are also patches of bright colours. Some creatures have wide, dark eyes and iridescent shimmerings that catch the light then fade just as fast, making it as hard to focus on a single animal through the microscope's eyepiece as it is to follow one animal among a stampeding herd. The stop–start spurts of speed and the wonderful whirligig and Catherine wheeling paths of the different species are mesmerising. The diversity can be overwhelming, especially as many animals go through various transformations as they grow, but certain types become recognisable once you get your eye in, such as the crab larvae with their carapace spines, compound eyes and their dainty legs gathered underneath them.

Barnacle larvae are remarkably similar to crab plankton, their legs clearly visible as they paddle their way across the Petri dish. At this stage in its development the young barnacle is clearly a crustacean, and I can only tell it apart from the crabs by looking at identification books. The animal under the microscope seems a million miles from the unmoving acorn barnacle shells attached to the rocks. The story of how this free-swimming creature turns into the barnacle we all recognise is almost as incredible as the story of the goose barnacle becoming a goose, only this one is true.

High up on any rocky shore, often even higher than the first limpets, there will be acorn barnacles. Small and numerous, they crowd together in their hundreds and thousands on suitable surfaces, blending in so well that it's easy to forget they are there at all. Their shells form mini mountain ranges and valleys between which green leaf worms and sea slaters roam. When they die, their empty tests provide perfect hidey-holes for minute sea snails like rough periwinkles.

I run my fingers over the sprawling barnacle city, feeling its sharpness and solidity. Here at the edges of the beach, the barnacles are pounded by the full might of incoming breakers, smashed and ground by water and rock, but still they cling on. Their secret is in their heads.

In the plankton, a young barnacle develops into a free-moving larva or cyprid, beating its long feathery legs to propel itself forward. Minute, but determined, the larva swims in search of a suitable place to settle, attracted to proteins that other barnacles have deposited on suitable rocks. When it finds its perfect spot, it settles head down on the rock and begins the process of transforming into an adult barnacle. At this stage it could easily be swept away by the waves and currents, so speed is of the essence. It begins producing a special substance which cements its head to the rock.

As you'd expect of an animal that has its head glued to a rock, once attached the barnacle will move little, if at all, for the rest of its life. The baby acorn barnacle now starts the process of building a strong home, made of overlapping plates, with an opening at the top shielded by door-like plates: the tergum and scutum. Each time the tide comes in, the barnacle opens these doors and extends its feathery legs. Sometimes you can see barnacles at work, their legs pulsing rhythmically, grabbing passing food and delivering it to their mouthparts. At all other times they are still and frozen, their days of swimming in the plankton long behind them.

These days, doing surveys of intertidal wildlife as a volunteer for our local Wildlife Trust, I spend hours on beaches trying to tell barnacle species apart based just on their shells. With practice it is possible, but still challenging. Acorn barnacles vary considerably depending on the surface they're on and how densely packed they are, their shape adapting to the barnacles around them. Several different species may also occur on the same rock.

There are clues in the number and shapes of the plates and the top opening, as well as their location. Those at the very top of the rocks are often *Chthamalus montagui*, a name with so many consonants piled up together I've never attempted it out loud. This species of barnacle can shut its aperture tightly to avoid drying out. Its attachment to the rock by a membrane instead of a calcified base may also help this barnacle to hold on through storms. Further down the rock, other species crowd in.

My favourite way to confirm a barnacle's species is by its colours. This might seem odd, given that they are all pretty much the same washed-out grey, but the trick is to wait for them to slide open their doors.

Barnacles are even less likely to survive being picked off a rock for examination than limpets, and they only slide their doors open when in water, so I focus on finding barnacles in a pool at the base of the rock or on smaller stones that I can place in water. Sometimes barnacles recently uncovered by the tide are also wet enough to remain part-open.

I crawl along, pressing my face close to the rock and using a hand lens to secure a good view. Rock pooling probably isn't the best pursuit for the self-conscious as I look deranged in this position, scrabbling about in the sand with my bottom in the air and muttering to myself. Fortunately, there are rarely many people about to notice. Although some people visit the beaches all year round, few of them bother with clambering about on the rocks as I have to do to access the animals. However strange I must appear, I don't mind because I know this will be worth it. I am looking to see if any of the animals has left its opening ajar, to reveal the colourful lining of its doors, the tergoscutal flaps. It takes patience. As soon as there's any disturbance, barnacles clamp their doors shut.

My knees and arms start to go numb as I wait and my eyes go fuzzy with the effort of staring, but I'm rewarded with a hint of movement as a barnacle prepares to extend its feeding legs. As the doors slide back, a thin lining along the door plates is revealed for a moment, a vivid electric blue with a flash of orange at the centre. These colours are typical of the *Chthamalus stellatus* barnacle. Other species are white, or yellow with brown spots: each has its own distinct combination. Some, like *Balanus crenatus*, even fluoresce under ultraviolet light. The colours are so unexpected they seem to belong to a different animal. Even the movement of the doors is fascinating, revealing that these stone-like lumps really are animals that breathe and feed like any other.

Barnacles turn up everywhere, adapting to so many different substrates and lifestyles that they constantly surprise me. Goose barnacles don't only grow on wood these days, but on anything that people leave floating in the sea, from glass and plastic bottles to fishing crates, buoys, ropes, nets and even shoes. The buoy barnacle looks similar to the goose barnacle, with its long neck and

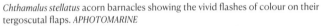

Chthamalus stellatus acorn barnacles showing the vivid flashes of colour on their tergoscutal flaps. *APHOTOMARINE*

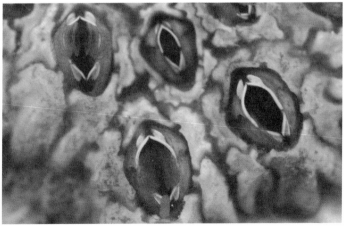

triangular plates, but creates its own float, a soft white bead which closely resembles a bead of polystyrene. When many are washed up at once it can be hard to tell what's plastic and what's not.

Acorn barnacles stick to almost anything hard, covering limpets, growing out of crab shells and fouling the bottoms of boats, causing unwanted extra drag. There are species that specialise in living embedded within sponges or on the rim of hard corals. The warped, asymmetric plates of the *Verruca stroemia* barnacles often adorn the inside of kelp holdfasts with their modernist sculptures. Other types of barnacles are stranger still, like those that grow in the deepest oceans near hydrothermal vents, surviving immense pressures. Some even live as parasites in the body of crabs.

The way in which barnacles often smother entire rock surfaces with their densely packed shells is testament to their reproductive success. It isn't easy to imagine something as immobile as a barnacle having sex, so in the world of underwater surprises this is one of the biggest, in more senses than one.

Whereas limpets develop from one sex to the other within their lifetimes, trying each out in turn, most barnacles are both male and female at the same time (hermaphrodites are relatively common in the marine world). This strategy means that every animal can release young, maximising their presence in the plankton and improving the chances of successful settlement. Although some barnacles are capable of fertilising themselves, they mostly fertilise each other.

Every acorn barnacle has both a penis, which is kept tucked in near the back of the feeding legs, and ovaries, which are found towards the base of the shell. A small acorn barnacle doesn't fertilise itself, but with its head cemented to the rock is unable to go off in search of a mate. Even though these barnacles live in close proximity to each other, forming a sheet of animals with few gaps, the distance from the aperture of one barnacle to the oviduct of the adjacent barnacle is often as big as the animal itself. If it wants to reproduce the barnacle must bridge that gap.

So, compared to the size of the animal, a barnacle has an enormously long penis. Some, like *Semibalanus balanoides*, even have a folded structure enabling them to stretch out even further. When fully extended, the penis may be up to eight times the length of the barnacle itself. The equivalent in humans would be a six-foot-tall male with a forty-eight-foot-long penis.

The barnacle has another problem. It can't see what it's doing. Undeterred, it blindly feels around the area to detect other barnacles and seek out their apertures. In this way, it will usually be able to fertilise several barnacles in its vicinity, and they will likely return the favour. Once its work is done, the barnacle will discard its penis, regrowing it again for the breeding season, which is around November or early December each year. To ensure that the young barnacles have the best chance of survival, the adult barnacle releases a special hatching substance as soon as it begins ingesting microscopic algae at the start of the spring plankton bloom. This substance triggers the release of its young into the seawater to coincide with high levels of available food.

Other types of barnacle don't live in such tightly packed communities and settle for a similar reproductive technique to the limpets, broadcasting their sperm into the water and hoping for the best. All these approaches seem to work, and a walk on any rocky beach will show you just how successful they are in colonising the shore.

Barnacles are as closely associated with the sea as buckets and spades. From leery drinking songs like Barnacle Bill, to the enraged outbursts of 'Blistering barnacles!' by seafaring children's characters like Captain Pugwash and Captain Haddock, barnacles have wheedled their way into our culture and language. They are so common on the rocky shore that the rocks themselves seem to be hewn from them, but they are far from uninteresting, hiding secrets behind those little bony plates and sheltering all sorts of creatures among their hills and hollows. No matter how many times I'm scratched by them when moving a rock or scrape my leg on their sharp tests, they never lose their intrigue.

CHAPTER 3

Common Prawn

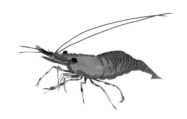

One summer, I made the mistake of rock pooling in open-toed sandals. It seemed like a good plan. The solid sole was sturdier than my usual neoprene beach shoes, giving me a firm grip on the slippery rocks and protection from sharp barnacle tests. As well as being cooler to wear than wellies, my sandals would also allow me to wade in up to my thighs, or even my waist, if I wanted to, and were far more comfortable to wear on hot days than my waders. What could go wrong?

As the tide slipped back, I stepped out to the edge of the rocks where the barnacles, limpets and seaweeds started to appear. Beyond this first ridge was a wide, shallow pool. The water was cold enough to make me wince, flooding over the sole of the sandal and between my toes, but I told myself that the pools would soon warm up in the sunshine. Standing still and waiting, I was rewarded with seeing a juvenile shore crab burying itself in the sand, shimmying the back of its shell deeper while shovelling at the sand with its pincers. I was reaching into my pocket for my camera when I felt something scrape against my foot.

Imagining I'd stirred up some pebbles or knocked my foot against a rock, I moved it backwards and carried on as before.

Seconds later I felt it again, a nipping, scratching sensation at the edge of my big toe. Looking down, I saw the culprits; a gang of four or five prawns were clustering around my foot, taking turns to shuffle forwards, snip at my skin with their pincers, then scuttle backwards, out of range. Without looking, I could feel that my other foot was under attack too.

Prawns are expert scavengers and cleaners, well known for stealing the leftovers from crabs' meals and nibbling the dead skin from fish. Watching them encircling my toes, I wondered if they might be protecting their territory from my invading foot. It was easier to think this than to accept the truth that the prawns were eyeing my foot as a potential meal. From the prawns' point of view, it was nothing personal. They didn't care who I was or how well washed my feet were, they couldn't help exploring every possible opportunity, even if it meant snacking on my toes.

No matter how much I shifted my feet about, the gang of prawns persisted in pursuing, following me relentlessly, keeping up their tickling and pinching until I could think of nothing else. Their numbers grew constantly, and it felt like the entire prawn population of the beach was after me. In the end, the only solution was to admit defeat and head home to find my wetsuit boots.

Annoying though over-friendly prawns can be, their natural curiosity makes them easy to watch. When I was a child exploring the pools in bare feet, I don't think I stayed still long enough to be nibbled by them. They were one of the few mobile creatures I'd see up close, because even if I splashed and screamed headlong into their pool, they'd still emerge a few moments later. Their long, yellow-striped claws and busy back legs fascinated me, as did the way they slapped down their powerful tails if you disturbed them, propelling themselves backwards through the water at high speed. Best of all, on the rare occasions I could manage to pick a prawn up, it would use its tail-slap to execute a spectacular jump and flip, somersaulting through the air and tumbling back to the pool with a noisy belly-flop landing.

Sometimes I'd spot a female carrying a clutch of eggs between her back legs, weighing her down so that she swam in an ungainly lopsided way. Lifting seaweed regularly made me squeal back then, and still does. Prawns like to lurk among the thick fronds of the wracks, so that when I plunge my hands in among the slippery tangle, searching for snails, a shower of prawns begins catapulting off in all directions.

Many species of prawn live from the midshore down because they cannot tolerate the great variations in temperatures, salinity, oxygen levels and food resources in the highest pools. However the common prawn, *Palaemon elegans*, has no such limitations. Its boldness and adaptability enable it to compete successfully for food in small pools where resources are limited. It also has a few tricks up its claws.

A curious prawn approaching my camera.

Common Prawn

If I lower my camera into a pool and wait, it often takes under a minute for prawns to start swimming closer, homing in on the strange object, reaching out with their pincers to give the lens a little tap. They observe everything keenly through shining eyes mounted on long stalks. Rather like flies and other insects, these compound eyes are made up of lots of separate photoreceptors, allowing light to come in from many angles at once, meaning that the prawn has a far wider field of vision than our own. Not much escapes their notice, especially something new in their pool. In turn, I can observe everything about them, almost down to the last meal they ate; their digestive organs are clearly visible through their transparent bodies. Although I have no intention of dissecting prawns to find out what they've been chomping on, my experience of watching them and of getting my feet nibbled suggests that they will go for absolutely anything available, from seaweeds to other crustaceans.

An insight into just how varied their diet can be was revealed by a study in 2008 by the Institute of Oceanography of the University of Gdansk. Researchers looked at the diets of *Palaemon elegans* in various locations in the Baltic Sea, an area which this resourceful prawn successfully colonised towards the end of the twentieth century. Predictably, the prawns in the study were found to be eating a wide variety of plant and animal foods such as seaweeds, detritus, sea mats, worms and small crustaceans. The balance of their diet varied enormously between different locations and times of year. Opportunistic as always, they didn't pass up on any chance to eat. Researchers discovered that in the early warm season, pine pollen, blown into the pools on the wind from coastal forests, was being eaten by the prawns. It was even the main component of the prawns' diet in locations where it was abundant. It is this flexibility which enables the prawn to survive through the changing seasons in pools where food can be limited.

The clever adaptations of the common prawn to the harsh intertidal environment don't stop there. At night, when the seaweeds stop photosynthesising, the oxygen levels in the pools can plummet, especially in the shallow waters at the top of the shore where the pools are not topped up with more oxygen-rich sea water for long periods. In summer a combination of high water temperatures and increased salinity due to evaporation can also reduce the amount of dissolved oxygen available to the animals for breathing. For most marine animals, such low levels of oxygen would be fatal, but *Palaemon elegans* has developed a solution which is highly effective.

When I first saw this behaviour, towards the end of a hot day in the pools, I thought the prawns were dead or close to death. Flopped, unmoving on the edge of the pool, sprawled on their sides with their limp bodies half-in, half-out of the water, they looked unwell at best. Closer inspection showed that they were beating their short back legs, but not their tails, suggesting that, despite their discomfort, they weren't making any effort to move back into the water. Within their transparent heads, something else was fluttering rapidly. They were clearly doing something to enable themselves to breathe in the hypoxic conditions of their pool. As the tide arrived to reclaim the pool, they slid back into it and become more active as though nothing had happened.

This technique of partially immersing themselves at the water's edge is unique and effective. The prawn's beating back legs draw oxygen from the air into the water and the fluttery device in its gill chamber also draws oxygen in with the water. They can even survive for several hours with almost no oxygen at all, becoming completely motionless.

Living in pools near the top of the shore limits the number of predators to which these prawns are exposed, which is why some choose this zone over the midshore. Although prawns are

The common prawn *Palaemon serratus*.

well-defended with pincers, they're no match for crabs or large fish which might fancy a meal, so they tend to rely on their tail-flick speed and camouflage to stay safe. It's handy being transparent. Hungry predators are likely to look straight through them, but these prawns have another trick that they can deploy to improve their camouflage. They can change colour to match their environment.

Looking down a microscope at a prawn was a surprising experience. I wondered if I needed to adjust the focus or check my eyes. The surface of the prawn was scattered with exploding star shapes in reds and golds that seemed to move before my eyes. I'd heard of chromatophores before, but I hadn't imagined these pigment spots to be so exciting. There were noticeable changes in the spots as the prawn adjusted to the light of the microscope, not least of all the increasing amount of yellow, matching the colour of the lamp light. Within a minute or two, small spots could expand into firework bursts of colour and vice versa, adapting to background colours and light levels, always working to blend in to the surroundings. Bold as they are, prawns are also adept at disappearing when they need to.

When running rock pooling events, I am always asked the difference between a shrimp and a prawn. One answer is that the snout-like rostrum at the front of the head is a different length in each. The common prawns, like *Palaemon elegans* and its cousin lower down the shore, the *Palaemon serratus*, have a long snout fringed with teeth along the top. They also sport stripy pincer arms splashed with bold yellows or blues. The common shrimp or brown shrimp, *Crangon crangon*, on the other hand, is a less colourful beast with its mottled browns and greys. It has a much shorter, blunter snout and shorter pincer legs.

Confusingly, although prawns have a long rostrum and the shrimps a short one, the two names are used interchangeably when people talk about these animals, so the names 'prawn' and 'shrimp' do not always correspond with this definition. For instance, the common prawn is also known as the glass shrimp, because of its transparent appearance. The animal sold as pink shrimp is a prawn, from the Processidae family. There's also a whole other group of animals commonly called mysid shrimps or opossum shrimps, that have a dozen or more short, feathered legs and no claws, which are in a completely separate order from both prawns and shrimps. They're small and hard to spot but often swarm around seaweed or anemones, swirling, hovering, separating and regrouping like a flock of minuscule birds.

The common shrimp is far more numerous on some beaches than the common prawn due to its preference for sand and mud. Although it can live out at sea and is sometimes fished commercially, the common shrimp is at home between the tides and can occur high on the shore where streams and rivulets in the sand and mud create pools and a soft substrate to hide in. It isn't able to cope with such major changes of environment as the common prawn and has a less adaptable diet.

There were plentiful shrimps in shallow sandy pools near the top of the shore at the beach near my childhood home. I loved to sit and splash in those pools enjoying their warmth after body boarding in the chilly sea, lying back as if they were a bath. If I stayed still for a while I could watch the shrimps scooting in jerky movements across the sand. Sometimes they would settle for a moment before frantically pedalling their back legs, kicking up a small sandstorm as they sunk their bodies down. After a few seconds, only their short eye-stalks were visible, sticking up like miniature tree stumps in a sandy desert. Even when I knew they were there, they were hard to see. If I took my eyes off them for a second, it was impossible to find them again among the swathes of similar coloured sand grains.

Despite its dull brown appearance, the common shrimp is a riot of chromatophores. Under the microscope they form tight constellations of white, brown and dark stars and splodges pressed in close to each other. Even at close range these patterns have a seventies' wallpaper effect, making it hard for your eyes to focus on any single part of the shrimp's mottled sides. These varying shapes and colours perfectly mimic the sandy or muddy background on which the shrimp lives, as well as breaking up its outline, making it harder for predators to spot or chase it.

I never tire of watching prawns and shrimp and they never seem to tire of anything. I can't imagine how they can spend so much time every day in their small rock pool worlds when they are clearly avid explorers, curious about everything. They seem to be like me in the way that they reach out and touch at the edges of their world. Through their glittering compound eyes, prawns take in hundreds of views of the world all at once. I look into those eyes and they look back. Then, with a flick of its tail, the prawn is gone.

CHAPTER 4

Shanny

The hole in the old harbour wall is at head height. I stand on tiptoes to look in, moving the position of my feet every few seconds as they sink into the oozing sand. The wall is rough, covered with barnacles, and there's a faint sulphurous smell, as though there's a volcanic vent nearby. The smell is coming from the anaerobic respiration of millions of bacteria in the muddy sand. The sea is over a hundred metres away and, other than the limpets and occasional beadlet anemone on this wall, it doesn't look like there's much life here.

Even though it's a bright day, I've brought my torch because the hole is deep and dark. I press my eye as close as possible to the hole, switch on the torch and peer in. Two fish almost the length of my hand gaze steadily out at me, their skin glistening and wet, their thick white lips pursed. Four eyes glow orange in the torchlight. This far away from the edge of the sea, any fish would normally be distressed and gasping, but the opposite is true for this pair of shannies. Lolling on their sides, they seem comfortable, thoroughly at home. These fish out of water are precisely where they want to be.

As young fish, shannies (also known as common blennies)

tend to be confined to the pools where they can easily hide among the seaweed or under boulders. As they grow, some will adopt a hole in the rock or in man-made structures like this harbour wall. So long as they remain in their damp shelters, out of reach of the sun and wind which might dry them out, they are able to survive out of the water. Although they mostly breathe through their gills, shannies are also able to directly absorb some oxygen from the air, breathing through their slimy skins. Slippery secretions on their skins keep them damp at all times. The shanny's almost amphibious quality, together with its ability to squirm and hop between pools, lend the fish its other common name, the sea frog.

Shannies will frequently return to the same hole at every low tide, making it easy to observe them if you know their favourite spots. When the hole is big enough, there will often be several fish in the same hiding place, piled on top of one another.

The shanny (common blenny) gives a smile for the camera.

The shanny, *Lipophrys pholis*, is a stalwart of the rock pool community, found in a huge variety of places, from the raised pools around the cliff edges to the deep hiding places of the lower shore. Like all blennies, the shanny has a single long dorsal fin instead of the two or three most other fish have. It is also easily distinguished from other blennies because it is the only one not to have any tentacles on its head. If you're patient, shannies are the easiest of all the rock pool fish to watch. In fact, few things can beat a sunny afternoon of gazing into clear water and coming nose-to-nose with busy blennies.

My top spot for blenny watching is Kynance Cove on the Lizard peninsula, the most southerly part of the UK mainland. There are hundreds of other beaches where you could do the same, but the imposing rock stacks and turquoise waters here are a great setting for lounging about watching fish.

The pools are high up, gouged into the snake-skin serpentinite rocks by the strong swell that washes in from the Atlantic. Unlike the slates, granites and softer rocks found around most of the British Isles, these cliffs have been thrust up from beneath the Earth's crust from the very edge of the mantle. Formed at immense temperatures and pressures, their red and green scaled surfaces create a unique shoreline, with rocks that wear smooth and provide few surfaces to which sea creatures can cling. Apart from the barnacles and a few anemones that stick to overhanging surfaces, it seems like there's not much here.

I clamber up the slippery rock to a plateau chiselled away by loose rocks from the bay, which are flung against these cliffs during storms. Behind a small ridge, a string of crystalline pools fringed with delicate pink coral weed stretches out before me. Unusually, this coral weed, *Corallina officinalis*, has a calcified structure, which makes its fronds hard and unappealing to herbivores. When it dies back the external colour is lost, leaving behind a white, bleached 'skeleton'. I settle in with the sun in front of me so as not to cast a shadow and wait.

The pool seems empty, the surface only slightly rippled by a light breeze. Towards the far edge of the pool, the bright white reflection of the sun glares back at the cloudless sky. Time passes unnoticed, the rhythmic rumble of the waves lulling me almost to sleep despite the constant shrieks of excited children playing in the sea. When my eyes refocus on the pool, looking past the surface reflection to the seaweeds below, I see a brief movement: the flash of a tail fin. The fish seems to disappear as quickly as it appeared, but by staring at the place I saw it, a shape begins to emerge.

Lying propped on the tripod-like prongs of its pelvic fins and its fanned pectoral fins, its eyes swivelling left and right, a young shanny is watching my every move. Its body is nestled among the coral weed, its colours camouflaging it perfectly. It rests, unmoving for a moment, before edging towards me.

Other heads pop up from under the rocky rim of the pool, until half a dozen shannies are gazing out. They all advance, bit by bit towards the surface, although none is as bold as the first shanny, which comes so close I can see a row of white teeth between its fat lips. They're crooked and disconcertingly human in appearance. Behind the teeth the gills are working away to keep the fish oxygenated in this small pool.

Waterproof cameras used to be inordinately expensive and required bulky casing, making them too cumbersome to use in the tight spaces of the rock pools, but my Olympus Tough camera is part of a new breed of more affordable and versatile devices. It fits in my pocket and manages good close-up shots with the macro settings, allowing me to take full-size photos of animals I can barely see with the naked eye. When I lower it into the water all the fish dart away, down under the safety of the rocky ledge. But within seconds I begin to see heads peeping out from between the stiff fronds of the coral weed. Like a game of grandmother's footsteps, the shannies close in, their movements quick and almost imperceptible. The brave fish is at the front once again and wins the game by being the first to touch my camera lens, giving it a few tentative headbutts before backing off to a comfortable position a few centimetres away, where it can keep a curious eye on the newcomer.

Almost wherever I am on the shore there are shannies in the pools. They will often find a vantage point in the pool like a large stone to lie on, pushing themselves up onto their fins to survey their territory, seeming not to fear any predators. Perhaps at low tide, when the large wrasse and other fish can't access these stranded pools, they are safe.

In the late spring the males turn darker with white lips as they prepare to guard the eggs, which the females lay as a thin coating on the underside of rocks. Like many doting fish dads, the shanny stays close to the eggs, seeing off predators that come too close with that nippy set of teeth. After a few weeks the eggs hatch into minute fry, which guzzle everything in sight and rapidly grow into little fish with disproportionately huge pectoral fins, so that they look like they should be able to fly.

As they grow still more, the young fish develop their camouflage spots and powerful teeth, enabling them to eat whatever is available in their pools. A favourite habit of the blennies is biting down on barnacles, either crushing their shells to eat them whole or nibbling off their feeding legs. They're not fussy, however, and are equally happy to eat other small invertebrates such as top shells, or to snack on seaweed.

Those teeth are not to be messed with and I've known even a small fish to give an unsuspecting rock pooler quite a nip. They're not an easy fish to pick up in any case as their skin is so slimy. If

I need to take one out of a bucket, I find they often don't mind a hand under their belly, enabling them to sit up and look at the outside world. I've never tickled a trout, but I imagine it's a similar feeling. Personally, I tend to leave shannies well alone in the pools. After all, if I need a close look at one, all I need to do is sit and wait for it to come to me.

The shanny isn't the only type of blenny on the shore. Some other species can air breathe too, but for shorter periods, so they seem to prefer the comfort of the pools rather than seeking out hiding places above the waves. The Montagu's blenny often occurs in relatively high pools, alongside the shannies. It's not so well recorded as it is smaller than the shanny and similar enough to go unnoticed. It also has a far shyer character, making it harder to watch. Any pool with plenty of acorn barnacles will do for trying to spot the Montagu's blenny, preferably one with comfortable rocks around it as it pays to be quiet and still.

Naturalists, by definition, tend to spend much of their time in isolated, wild places, and opportunities to share experiences face to face with like-minded people can be rare. So arriving in the early morning for a Bioblitz – when the field or village hall is buzzing with the chatter of people of all ages as they gather around tables filled with microscopes, information stands and chalk boards – brings a sense not just of excitement but of legitimacy.

The atmosphere was palpable at my first Bioblitz in July 2014 at Kingsand and Cawsand, overlooking Plymouth Sound, as we waited for the 24-hour marathon of wildlife recording to start. There were kids in bright waterproof jumpsuits, people carrying bags of live mammal traps, butterfly nets and sampling quadrats and, just for once, I felt completely at home in my waders, hair flying in my eyes, balancing a precarious assortment of trays and buckets.

Experts from almost every field of nature recording were there: ornithologists, botanists, mycologists, herpetologists, mammalogists, lepidopterists, entomologists, marine biologists to name just the ones I can spell, and many had travelled from far afield. These surveys are always well attended by the public too, especially those who live nearby and are curious to discover the secrets of their surroundings or bring local knowledge to guide us to the best spots. Watching Junior hopping away across the rocks with some new friends, I wondered whether I might have returned to Cornwall sooner, or never have left, if there had been similar opportunities to meet so many enthusiasts and to see people earning their living in the environmental sector when I was his age. In this inclusive gathering, our only focus was our shared goal to record as many species as possible within the 24-hour time limit. As my partner, Ed, aptly put it, I had found 'my people'.

We gathered around the map of the designated area, assembled into groups for the first activities, and awaited the starting orders. I was surrounded by keen rock poolers and professional marine biologists, all sharing tips on purchasing the best waders, constructing a plankton trawl net using an old pair of tights or making the perfect seaweed lasagne. We were joined by families and students who were all raring to explore the beach. With this many pairs of eyes together, with a broad range of expertise and plenty of kit to play with, we were almost guaranteed to see something new.

My intention was to walk straight out to the lower shore, where the greatest diversity of species would be, but the first pools I came to, with their fringes of coral weed and buzzing communities of prawns, shannies and anemones, stopped me in my tracks. The clear water and warm sunshine were perfect for staring into pools and there was still plenty of time until low tide. Like most things in life, rock pooling is best when it's unhurried.

Montagu's blenny with its distinctive headgear.

Bang in the centre of the shallow pool, a blenny was sunbathing on an elevated rock, its head grazing the surface. While it scanned its surroundings, the only sign of movement it gave were its swivelling eyes, each turning independently, on the lookout for food or danger, or perhaps just watching the world go by. Among the green strands of gutweed at the edge of the pool, a prawn hovered, exploring something with its pincers beneath the barnacle-covered rock edge. The flicker of another fish caught my eye as it darted out of the weed.

It rested in the shadow of a stone, its body side-on to me. I could just see the long fin on its back. A small blenny. I was struck by the pale blue spots on its body, overlying vertical dark stripes. It was an especially prettily marked shanny, I thought. The fish edged out from the rock, poking its head through some seaweed to see if the coast was clear. I leaned in closer and screwed my eyes against the reflection from the water's surface. The fish was only as long as my little finger, so it was hard to be sure, but it seemed to have something akin to a small Christmas tree growing out of its head.

Intrigued, I coaxed it into a tub so I could take a better look. Close-up, the appendage looked rather like a pronged TV aerial set upright on the blenny's head. I've never been sure why some species of blenny have these head tentacles, as they're called, but the number and shape of the tentacles is the surest way to tell most species apart. This one was a Montagu's blenny.

I released the fish back into the pool and watched it moving from one spot to another, looking from a distance just like another shanny, of which there were several in the pool. It lingered near the clumps of barnacles, its favourite food – when the tide comes in and the barnacles open, the Montagu's blenny likes to nibble off their legs.

From the highest holes in a harbour wall to the pools and the furthest reaches of the shore, blennies are always close by. They are with me on every perfect rock pooling day, lounging in patches of shimmering sunlight, looking out of the water as I look in. They demand my full, unswerving attention, a state of yogic concentration and calm. Only then will they come close and mirror my gaze. The slightest movement and they vanish, darting away like projectiles, too fast for my eyes to follow. And from the darkness of their hiding places, they carry on watching.

CHAPTER 5

Sandhopper

Anyone who has ever played in the sand, building castles, walls, moats and defences, will probably have met sandhoppers by the dozen. I watch Junior scooping dry, white sand into a towering volcano shape as tall as his five-year-old self. The sides are so high and steep that the strong sea breeze scrapes at them, forming a vortex of sand on one side. Sand skitters and tumbles down the edges of his volcano almost as fast as he adds more to the top and with it come the tiny bodies of the sandhoppers, popping out from between the grains, writhing to free themselves then leaping through the blowing sand and tumbling down near my son's feet.

Some of the escaped sandhoppers carry on leaping, covering the distance to the sand dunes or the tideline in a series of phenomenal bounds, taking off with great force, shooting high then tumbling, suspended in mid-air for a moment, before crashing into the soft sand. Others lower their heads and work their limbs, showering sand up behind them as they tunnel down and hide. When I scan the sand around me, what at first seemed like a featureless expanse of grains reveals a secret community. I notice one hole, then another, and soon see them everywhere.

The hiding holes and burrows of hundreds of sandhoppers, and probably some other shoreline invertebrates too, are hidden beneath my feet forming a vast network. They hide here, backfilling their holes when the tide comes in to stop the water from flooding their homes.

We capture sandhoppers in our hands as they emerge from the volcano and hold them for a few seconds, so light that they feel like air until they wriggle and flick against our hands, trying to jump free. We open our palms and watch them spring away, blown off-course by the breeze as they tumble down the beach.

The sandhoppers are part of the amphipod family, animals with laterally compressed bodies that look thin from the top, some of which live above the tideline and need to breathe air, while other species need to be in the water most or all the time. We walk away from the sandcastle, alongside the piles of dried and twisted seaweed of the tideline, untangling pieces of bright plastic and nylon fishing line from the detritus as we go and slipping it into a bag. There are more sandhoppers among the treasures thrown up by the waves. I pick up the empty egg case of a small spotted catshark and, when we press its sides and peer in, a sandhopper wriggles and springs away onto the sand. They are under the drinks cans we pick up, inside the broken plastic bottles, and as I remove a section of discarded fishing net, dozens of them tumble and scatter, bouncing around my hand, so that I have to shake the net for a full minute and pull every last piece of seaweed away to make sure the sandhoppers are gone.

When I was small, I used to be wary of sandhoppers. Their squashed bodies, delicate legs and even those unmoving compound eyes made me sure that they must be a type of flea. Some people even called them sand fleas. Sitting on the edge of the dunes with my bare legs against the hot sand, I would worry that a sandhopper would sneak up out of its burrow and bite my ankles. I'd watch them warily when they jumped too close, and if one leapt onto me I would be poised ready to flick it away if it took a nibble. None ever did bite though, so I gradually came to trust them.

It was many years later, when I first got hold of a proper seashore book from a bookshop in London between meetings, that I realised that these 'sand fleas' were about as closely related to the fleas as I am to the gulls. The fleas that bite us are, of course, a type of insect, whereas sandhoppers are an amphipod, a crustacean. Although sandhoppers have a similar body plan to fleas, the similarities between the two animals are a coincidence of their having evolved to jump. Both are able to perform amazing leaps of many times their own body length. Sandhoppers, however, are in the same group as the prawns, crabs and sea slaters. There are some crustaceans that bite, but the common sandhopper, *Talitrus saltator*, is not among them.

Piles of rotting seaweed teeming with hopping crustaceans may not seem attractive, but it is an essential part of the beach ecosystem. Seaweed can be smelly and it's always full of flies and other creepy-crawlies, so on many tourist beaches a tractor is sent in every day to trawl all the unsightly tideline debris into a heap to be disposed of or buried in the sand. Among this heap will be litter, which has no place on the beach and is best removed, but when seaweeds and other detritus are taken away, the nutrients that provide the basis of the intertidal food chain are taken with them, adversely affecting a web of organisms from seabirds to crabs. Removing the seaweed can have a devastating effect on local ecosystems.

The clue to the sandhopper's role in the ecosystem is in the concentration of these animals along the tideline. When they

The common sandhopper *Talitrus saltator*.

emerge from under the sand, they are drawn towards anything the tide has left behind. By feeding on all manner of detritus, they break it down. Along with other animals and microbes, they effectively clean the beach of debris. Amphipods are eaten in turn by seabirds, fish, prawns and crabs, and they in turn by larger crabs, fish and other predators. Amphipods are key to the decomposition process, which provides energy across the whole food chain. If the seaweed is removed from a beach, then nutrients drop for all the intertidal community and fewer animals will survive.

Some councils and beach owners now only remove tideline debris during the peak tourist months, which can help the beach ecosystem and reduce costs, but it would still be far better to leave the beach alone. Perhaps, with greater awareness, people will change their concept of what a clean beach is.

The strandline sandhoppers are not the only type of amphipod on the shore. My current go-to book, the *Handbook of the Marine*

Fauna of North-West Europe by Peter J. Hayward and John S. Ryland, is far more detailed than my first seashore guide and lists 96 species of amphipod, but points out that more than 300 species have been found in the waters around the UK. They are not always easy to tell apart and I've spent many a happy hour staring down a microscope at these little creatures. They delight in doing frantic circles in a Petri dish while I try to spot miniscule features of their legs or tails. Mostly I give up.

Some amphipod species are so distinctive, however, that they are easily identified. My favourite is unmistakeable and, although it lives in the water, it prefers life even further from the sea than the sandhopper, favouring salt marshes and brackish pools.

This amphipod is impressive. I sometimes visit the salt marshes of estuaries just to see it. For a start, it has a cool name: *Corophium volutator*. It's an imposing name; the sort of name you can imagine a gladiator having. It suggests some kind of superpower: the power of volutating, whatever that might be.

Salt marshes can be treacherous, but fortunately these amphipods are happy in pools fringed with plenty of vegetation, so there's no need to wade through waist-deep mud to reach them (unless you like that sort of thing). Wellies and a good washing machine for your clothes afterwards are all that's required.

I edge as close to the pool as I dare, not wanting to end up in the mud. Salt marshes can be extremely stinky if you fall in. It is hard to see the amphipods straight away because their colouring blends in well with the mud, so I look for straight trails gouged in the mud. These are often a sure sign that *Corophium volutator* is nearby.

It doesn't take long. In the right locations these amphipods can live at immense densities of up to 100,000 per square metre. Most salt marsh pools I visit seem to have at least a few.

A male *Corophium volutator* edges across the mud, exactly what I'd hoped for. The animal's body is under two centimetres long, so I need to lean over the pool to see it. It looks bigger though, because extending out in front of its head are two enormous, chunky antennae, giving it more the appearance of a lobster than a sandhopper.

It is incredible that this animal can move at all; it is so front heavy. Its antennae are about the same length as its body and so sturdy they must pull the animal off balance. It uses them to feel its way along the mud, searching for microscopic foods like bacteria and diatoms. Like its shoreline cousins, it is perfectly designed for burrowing, digging holes in the mud, from which you can see the antennae protruding. Mature females tend to hide in these burrows. Males seek them out, entering their burrows and waiting for them to shed their outer skins in order to mate.

Even though they are clumsy swimmers, they are often found paddling about in the open water, especially on big tides, making them highly vulnerable to the shrimp, crabs, gobies and wading birds that like to feed on them. Perhaps, given that they only live for a year, it's a risk worth taking to find a mate or new food

Corophium volutator. Steve Trewhella

sources. Mostly, though, they are found resting in their burrows or crawling out across the mud, their long antennae dipping in and scouring a trail as they go.

The marine world is full of body shapes that seem improbable to land dwellers. In the water, the dynamics of weight and size work differently from the terrestrial world, but animals like this still have to be seen to be believed.

Back at the beach, I only need to move just beyond the tideline, to the rocks that are washed by the sea every day, to find yet more species of amphipods. Pick up any stone embedded in the wet sand and there will often be a squirming mass of them underneath. With a close look, it is easy to see how these animals get the name amphipod, which comes from the Greek words for 'around' and 'foot'. They often have quite a variety of legs, from short to long, tapered to clawed, smooth to feathery. Careful examination of these limbs and of their antennae is often necessary to work out what species of amphipod you are looking at.

They look helpless, lying on their sides and wriggling. People often mistake them for prawns due to their many legs and pinkish colour, but they have neither the long nose-like rostrum of the prawn, nor its fanned swimming tail. Comma-shaped and soft-looking, these amphipods have the vulnerable appearance of a shelled prawn.

Unsurprisingly, they are eaten by many shore animals, from anemones and worms to gulls, and this is perhaps why they are constantly reproducing. Look closely at the squiggling shapes of the animals and you will often see that they are not one, but two. The larger males carry the females underneath them, mating when the female has moulted her skin-like shell. Often, I find myself looking down on a complete orgy, there are so many pairs gathered together under the shelter of the stone.

Some of these amphipods have been found to have a role in breaking down not only the organic material on the beach, but also the plastic debris. *Orchestia gammarellus* is able to shred plastic bags into tiny particles. These can then be ingested by the amphipods or other marine organisms, with the potential to build up throughout the marine environment. This is no longer just a problem concerning the ingestion of large pieces of plastic by seabirds and marine turtles; zooplankton have been filmed consuming microplastics, suggesting that all animals in the marine food chain are likely to be affected, as well as those terrestrial animals that eat them, such as humans.

In addition to the general risks to the health of animals that consume plastic in place of food, pollutants can build up on the surfaces of microplastics, especially persistent organic pollutants (POPs) such as solvents, pesticides and pharmaceuticals. These chemicals don't break down easily and concentrations tend to increase the longer the pieces of plastic spend in the sea. If animals ingest these pollutants, the quantities of POPs will increase as they go up the food chain, potentially contaminating or killing larger predators like fish and marine mammals. Removing plastics from the environment becomes harder as they are broken down into small pieces and mix with the water and sediment. The realisation that amphipods, and perhaps other marine animals, speed up the breakdown of plastics, makes finding ways to prevent plastics entering our oceans all the more urgent.

It is remarkable that an animal as small as a sandhopper is so essential to the well-being of the entire shore ecology. Every time I remove rubbish from the beach, I think of how easily it could break down and enter the bodies of these creatures and all the other animals that consume them. Whether I walk across a salt marsh, along the dunes or among the damp pebbles below the tideline, amphipods are often the first animals I see. Their unique body shapes and intriguing habits are a perfect launching point into the always-surprising underwater world that is uncovered as the tide retreats. That they are connected in so many ways to the rest of the marine environment adds to their fascination, drawing me ever closer to the underwater world.

CHAPTER 6

Beadlet Anemone

If you grow up in the countryside, you have to be good at entertaining yourself. In the absence of cinemas, shops and common sense, my little group of friends and I would explore every last centimetre of the trees, quarries, dunes, cliffs and beaches that made up our little world. So long as we stayed out of the sea and turned up at home in time for tea, our parents didn't worry. Mawgan Porth was the sort of village where news travelled fast, so we couldn't get away with much, although we often ignored the warnings about climbing up to the cliffside mine workings, which constantly dribbled out a trickle of bright orange water. In the winter we could build forts from the mounds of foam that blew off the stormy seas and, once in a rare cold snap, we were able to slide on frozen sheets of water and snap huge, ridged icicles from the walls of ice that encased the cliffs. Through the summer we paddled in warm pools and jumped on the crumbling sand banks along the river and all year round the rock pools beckoned. One of our many fascinations was anemones. We were attracted to their colours at first, intense splashes of crimson against the grey rock, glowing with tropical brightness.

It is no accident that so many of these animals are named

after all that is wealth and beauty. Jewel, gem, dahlia, daisy, strawberry, elegant, starlet. The names are a joy to say out loud. Gem anemone, gem anemone, gem anemone. Even the common beadlet anemone is aptly named, sporting a string of beads around its wide ruby-red neck.

Defenceless though these squidgy lumps of jelly may seem, they are surprisingly robust. Beadlet anemones often occur as far up the shore as the limpets. They don't have a hard shell for protection against drying out, so they need to hide beneath overhangs or in holes in the rocks, often clinging to the base of the rocks where they sit in the pools at low tide.

Aged nine or ten, my schoolfriends and I would crouch by the rocks, taking turns to reach out and poke the anemones, feel them shiver against our fingers and watch the mouth pulling in tight. Sometimes the blobs were crimson red, sometimes a deep bottle green; fragile, yet clinging to the rock with great strength.

Hitching up our trousers, we waded into the deeper pools, where open anemones provided a display of floral brilliance against the yellow sand, their tentacles reaching in all directions. If you were close enough, you could see them twisting and grasping at invisible particles in the water. Though they looked like flowers, they behaved more like hungry triffids, always ready to grab any unsuspecting prey that passed. If we were lucky, we'd find an anemone with something hanging out of its mouth; an amphipod or the trailing tail of a polychaete worm. If we were really lucky, it would still be wriggling.

Of course, it's best not to disturb or poke creatures on the beach, but being young and curious, we couldn't resist putting our fingers into the water until they connected with the tentacles. Instantly, the anemone would stick and pull, making us snatch our hands away and giggle, before doing it all again. The sensation was strange, like being caught in a moving spider's web, and we were convinced the anemone was trying to eat us, even though we were many times its size.

We were right that it was attacking us. Anemones are cnidarians, which means that they belong to the same family as jellyfish and corals; animals that have stinging cells. Anemones deploy their attack strategy as soon as any potential food brushes their tentacles. These aren't just stinging hairs like nettles have though, this is the marine environment, and everything is that bit more extreme.

Within their tentacles, anemones have special cells called nematocysts, each containing a barbed harpoon on a coiled thread. These harpoons are equipped with a powerful toxin. As soon as these cells are triggered by something brushing against them, they fire out with explosive force, lodging themselves in whatever animal is unfortunate enough to be passing, paralysing their victim with venom. That sticky feeling when our fingers touched the anemone was caused by numerous harpoons firing into our skin.

Fortunately, the stings of most anemones aren't strong enough to affect humans, but it's always a good idea to avoid touching your eyes after contact with the cnidarian. Our skin may not be bothered by the toxins, but those little harpoons can easily be transferred to the delicate membrane of our eyeball, which is more sensitive. When I take groups rock pooling for our local Wildlife Trust or Marine Group, I warn children not to touch the anemones because of this risk and feel more than a little hypocritical. I still love that sticky feeling and seeing those tentacles at work.

My local secondary school probably wasn't such a dire place as I thought it was, but it felt to me like someone had scooped me out of the sea and was holding me in a bucket. In class, while I doodled clocks and coloured in the minutes or sketched the tentacles onto lopsided drawings of anemones, I dreamed of the open cliff paths, the shores, the sea and what lay beyond. I think we all felt it. Most of us were bussed in from our villages and farms, leaving behind our previous experiences of small primary schools with plenty of outdoor space and time. I escaped in my mind by dreaming and by latching onto subjects that reached out into the world: languages, music, geography, biology and literature. Some of the other kids were more blatant, bringing their surf boards on the school bus and talking the driver into dropping them at a beach half a mile before the school stop. I made lifelong friends among the pupils and staff, but nothing could lift my sense of confinement, that these were largely wasted days. Five years is forever when you're young.

Out of school I tried to keep up my environmental enthusiasm, gathering a bunch of village friends with similar interests into a rather militant group to pick up some of the endless stream of drinks cans, fishing lures, plastic drums and polystyrene that piled up on the tideline alongside the black clods of solidified tar that were still washing up from the *Torrey Canyon* oil disaster, over two decades after the tanker sank.

I remember an elderly and exceptionally grumpy neighbour who liked to sit in his front porch, which he'd built himself from a ship's cabin almost as old as he was. From his perch there, high on the cliffs, he could see for miles and easily spot people to grumble at. I tried to make sure it wasn't me, but when he talked about the horrific oil slick that had choked our local beach and hundreds of miles of other beaches around Cornwall and northern France, he had my attention. He described the horrendous thick black coating, the hopeless efforts to clear the oil by hand. He always said it wasn't necessarily the oil itself that did the worst damage, but the effort to clear it. First the government bombed the stricken tanker and even used napalm to try to burn the oil off the surface, then they began to try to break up the oil by spraying beaches with detergent and even rolling barrels of the stuff off cliffs. Everyone who could help in any way mucked in, shovelling oil off beaches and cleaning oiled seabirds. People even travelled to the area just to help; possibly the first movement of eco-volunteers in Britain.

What people didn't understand at the time was that the detergents being used to clear the oil were highly toxic to wildlife, including the micro-organisms in the environment that would naturally break down oil if left to their own devices. Beaches where the dispersants were used actually took far longer to recover than those which were left alone. The treated oil clumped into great lumps of tar that continued resurfacing and was still very much a feature of Cornish beaches in the 1980s and 90s when I was growing up, although it now only appears after the worst storms.

Even as the tar gradually diminished, my friends and I came across a new problem with oil, caused by boats washing out their tanks at sea. These mini-slicks caught on the feathers of diving and swimming birds, stripping them of their natural waterproofing and leaving them cold and exhausted. Sometimes we rescued oiled sea birds, running home to collect cardboard boxes to stuff them in, before persuading our parents to drive them to the RSPCA centre. But more often we found dead birds; guillemots and gannets lying limp-necked on the sand. Occasionally there were other animals like dolphins, seals or even a whale washed up, the cause of death unknown, shifting with each tide and reeking horrendously.

We called ourselves the Beach Bugs and spent many happy hours designing logos. We wrote to the council, conducted surveys among sunbathing tourists about bin provision, made home-drawn posters of trapped wildlife and jumped on cans to crush them on my parents' kitchen floor. Our work appeared in the local papers, but most people thought we were wasting our time and told us so. Like many other coastal areas, unemployment was high, the houses were being picked off one by one as second homes, and there was a grudging acknowledgment that tourism was the only way to survive. No one denied that the area lacked the infrastructure to deal with the litter, sewage and other environmental pressures that came with tourism but this, they said, was a price we would have to pay. Other marine litter and oil came from boats which shed their waste or washed out their tanks with impunity, too far from land to be seen or caught. We removed all we could, but some fishing nets were too heavy and it wasn't easy to persuade the council to collect the waste.

I'm sure I should have done more. I tried because I worried for the future of our rock pools full of delicate seaweeds and flower-like anemones, but trying was not enough. The rubbish kept coming. Before long we were all turning into self-conscious teenagers and other, less wholesome, interests were calling us. The feeling that I gave up still nags me, but all these years later there is a new wave of awareness, one that both adults and young people are on board with. The swell of interest and activism began to grow around the time I left home, when Surfers Against Sewage was a new organisation, just beginning to make a name for itself.

And all this effort is finally making a difference. The beach I cleaned with the Beach Bugs now has a team of volunteers doing regular litter picks. A permanent set of buckets and collection bins are set out where people enter the beach to encourage everyone to help out, and social media is rallying people to join the well-attended beach cleans, which also have the support of local businesses. When my son and I recently found a large net dumped by the receding tide, passers-by didn't think twice about stopping to help us haul it off the beach. Thanks to EU legislation and the work of campaign groups, there is also less pollution from rivers and sewage waste. The amount of debris and nets from fishing and shipping is worse than ever though, and there is much work to do.

Regardless of all these influxes of rubbish and oblivious to people's efforts to clean the shore, the anemones cling sedately to the rocks as they have always done, opening and closing with the tides. Like some other animals of the upper reaches of the intertidal zone, anemones don't seem to do much. Of course, they're not going to win many races, but anemones are more mobile than they seem at first sight. They can use the strong sucker on the base of their column to move about, shifting into more sheltered spots to avoid the sun and wind or to find better places to feed, and they are highly territorial animals. In the competitive environment at the top of the beach, where suitable damp and sheltered spots are at a premium, the beadlet anemone has evolved a special approach to defending its home against intruders.

Look closely at an open anemone and you will see, outside the circle of stinging tentacles, a ring of sky-blue beads. These are the beadlets which give this anemone its name. These acrorhagi, as they're officially known, are not just pretty; they are armed with a high concentration of nematocysts, more than are needed to stun prey. They are fighting tentacles and the anemones don't hesitate to use them.

If another anemone comes too close, the beadlet anemone will shuffle and nudge against it, shoving it to one side in slow motion. Lifting its side, it will bash down repeatedly on the other anemone with its acrorhagi. Its competitor may retaliate, and it can take days for the battle to play out, but the cumulative effect of the stings will eventually drive one of the anemones off, forcing it to squidge away and find another place to settle.

In this side view it is easy to see the blue beadlet tentacles that give this anemone its name and which are used for fighting.

Sometimes you can find anemones that are mid-battle, squashing against each other or leaning on each other mid-bash, but mostly they are closed. The high surface area of their tentacles makes them vulnerable to drying, so they keep them tucked in.

Perhaps the strangest thing of all about the beadlet anemone is its mouth. It's just a round, unexciting opening in the top of the animal, but it does far more than eat. The anemone has no other openings than the mouth. Its base is attached to the rock and all round it is just a blob with no other way in or out. Therefore, what goes in must come out and the anemone's mouth is also its anus.

The mouth also has a role in reproduction. Not only does the male anemone release sperm through the mouth, but the female receives it through hers. What happens next is even more bizarre, and is something I would just love to see for myself one day. The anemone grows the babies in a brood chamber until they are a few millimetres long and fully equipped with a small set of tentacles. She then spits her babies out of her mouth, projecting them into the water where they fall and settle.

Even in the absence of sperm, when a beadlet anemone is kept on its own in a tank, for instance, it seems that it will still produce young in this way, suggesting that these anemones may be able to reproduce asexually if needed.

Occasionally I find other species of anemone that can reproduce in yet another way. Jewel anemones, which are more closely related to corals than to the other anemones, have tentacles capped with tiny rounded beads. Sometimes I find one that seems bigger than the others, drawn out in a long ellipse instead of the usual neat circle and with more tentacles. If the anemone is open, I can look into its centre and see that it has two mouths. This is an anemone that is reproducing by longitudinal fission. It is splitting apart down its centre, tearing itself in two to create a whole new anemone, a clone of itself which looks identical in size, shape and colour. Eventually the twin anemones will break apart completely. This method of reproducing is why I often see clusters of jewel anemones all in the same hue, even though jewel anemones can vary greatly in colour from pink to turquoise. These anemones are likely to all be clones of each other, living side by side.

Due to their aggressive nature and deadly toxins, it's understandable that few things eat anemones. There is, however, a voracious predator that will sometimes venture well up the shore, even to some of the highest pools, in search of anemones to eat, and beadlets are among its favourites. Improbable as it may seem, the anemone's most feared enemy is a slug.

The shallow clear-watered pools of a sheltered bay are ideal for observing anemones at their best. Alongside the beadlet anemones, smaller gem anemones nestle in sandy cracks in the rock. Their brilliant lime-green and shocking-pink mouths are encircled by a wide star of striped tentacles, visible from many metres away despite their diminutive size. I crouch at the edge of the pool, leaning in to take a closer look, watching to see if any other animals are hiding nearby.

Thin threads of pale yellow extend and contract, spreading across the sand, sticky and feeling for prey. These are the tentacles of a worm, hidden somewhere beneath the surface, hoping to draw down a meal. If something brushes them, the tentacles are gone in an instant, curling in on themselves and slipping into the sand, sucked up like spaghetti.

Part-wedged under an overhang, a piece of slate about the size of my hand catches my attention. Anything solid with a gap underneath is a prized hiding place for shore creatures, which are always anxious to hide away from predators and to shelter from the drying sun and wind. I tease it out, watching a prawn flick away into the delicate strands of seaweed. Underneath the slate is a layer of white jelly, painted in a spiral shape, much like a child's drawing of a snail shell. These are the eggs of the great grey sea slug (*Aeolidia* sp.), a sure sign that the adults are nearby.

Half a metre away, hidden among some pink coral weed, I find the slug, looking fluffed up like a tiny sheep, due to the dense crop of shaggy cerata that are growing out of its back. It is feeling its way through the pool with the aid of two tentacle projections that emerge from the front of its head, and on top of its head it sports a fine pair of long antennae, known as rhinophores. It doesn't move anywhere fast, but it doesn't need to, relying instead on camouflage and chemical warfare to avoid harm.

Seashore identification books will generally tell you that this slug is white, but from the red-wine colour of this specimen, I know straight away that it has not long since had a meal. Just a few centimetres long, it's hard to imagine how this tiny animal has laid spawn several times its own size, let alone eaten an anemone, but that is exactly what has happened. Like in the stories of people who eat so many carrots they turn orange, the great grey sea slug feasts on anemones and takes in their pigment, turning its cerata brown, red or pink, perfect for hiding among the seaweed.

In addition to nutrition and colour, this sea slug has taken something else from its prey. Much like the anemone itself, the slug is naturally soft, squishy and easy prey for better-armed predators like crabs and fish. Its solution is to use the same defences as the anemone: stinging nematocysts. These soon deter any animal that chooses to take a nibble. The slug's problem, however, is that it is unable to produce these stinging cells on its own, so it borrows them. Each time it munches on an anemone, it passes the nematocysts in its food straight to its fluffy cerata. As a result, the slug's cerata don't only look like the fluffed-up tentacles of an anemone. They sting like one too.

Sometimes I find a great grey sea slug mid-meal, its head buried in the middle of an anemone many times its own size,

This great grey sea slug has recently eaten an anemone and has turned pink.

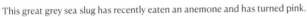

Beadlet Anemone

showing the kind of lack of restraint you see in attempts to set world records in burger eating. I'm torn between the amazement of seeing the slug change colour, the disappointment at the destruction of something so beautiful as the anemone and a kind of fascinated horror. I love both the anemone and the slug, but there's no hope of mediation between the two. In nature there is no right and wrong, no creature is more deserving or more worthy. In this complex and delicate web of survival, everything has its place, and the strategies creatures employ in this arms race only become more extreme the further out to sea I step, as more and more different animals mingle together, co-operating and competing for survival.

I replace the stone with the spawn, ensuring it is exactly as I found it, cover the sea slug once more in the seaweed where it was hiding. Whether the fabulous colours of the beadlet anemones will be here the next time I visit or whether they will have succumbed to the attentions of a new generation of slugs, only time will tell. It is hard to accept that no outcome is better or worse and that one animal's loss is another's gain, but I leave nature to take its course. Although these anemones have weathered the dangers of storms, oil spills, pollution and slug attacks before and have always bounced back so far, I worry that even these hardy creatures must have their limits.

CHAPTER 7
Shore Crab

I had ambitions to become a zoologist or marine biologist until I arrived for my trial week at sixth form college. I was nearly sixteen and as a keen linguist, I knew I would take French and German A level. Biology was the obvious choice of third subject. When I entered the biology lab for my taster session, I noticed immediately that it was darker than most the other classrooms. It took my eyes a while to adjust as we filed in. There was an aging, unnatural smell about the place, and some sort of lingering chemicals were engrained in the benches, making me crave fresh air.

My secondary school, though not always the most inspiring environment, at least had colourful posters of cells on the walls and, with the webbed feet of herring gulls constantly flopping their way across the reinforced skylights, we were never far from the natural world. In an alcove next to my school's science classrooms, one of the teachers even kept an eclectic assortment of reptiles, arachnids and insects in glass vivaria. Nothing broke the monotony of school life better than the escape attempts of the Chilean rose tarantula or the various snakes.

There was none of this sense of life in the sixth form science wing.

I had been in the classroom for several minutes, listening to the teacher's presentation about the syllabus, when my wandering gaze travelled upwards and rested on a shelf that ran around the room. There sat fluid-filled jars containing animals, or what was left of them. I think there was an oddly soft-looking pale crab among them and some of the life forms looked as though they might have been taken straight from the womb. Their strangled colours, saggy contours and awkward postures are all I remember. I was no stranger to the horrors and cruelties of the natural world and was as passionate then as I am now about investigating and understanding wildlife, but I was sickened as never before by this morbid display and knew instantly that I would not be spending two years studying in this room. The science of life was not for me. In my next taster lesson, the politics teacher did headstands, told jokes and encouraged us to question everything. I made many new life-long friends that week, including my partner, Ed, although it took us more than a decade to get together. Putting biology studies firmly behind me, I took politics and languages, which were to lead me out of my familiar world to travel to far-flung places and to take on policy work in land-locked capitals. I would manage to steer my career towards working on environmental issues, but it was a long while before I returned to the shore.

I find myself surrounded by children, all clutching empty margarine tubs, splashing through shallow pools, and crouching to scoop up creatures. I am lucky enough these days that my summers are full of public rock pooling events like this one. As soon as the shrieks and squeals start, I know one of the children has found a crab. I also know what sort it will be.

The green shore crab, *Carcinus maenas*, has to be one of our most successful marine creatures, as well as one of the best known. It's the crab you're most likely to find in rock pools, among the seaweed, clinging to crab nets dangled from a harbour wall or lurking in the mud of an estuary. A relative of mine even found an eerie graveyard of dead shore crabs crammed in the boot cavity of a second-hand car he bought. How they got there is a mystery, but it fits; shore crabs are not afraid to explore new places, whatever the consequences.

Sure enough, children are soon crowding round me to show off their crabs, many of which are tiny juveniles. In the pots are orange crabs, speckled crabs, pale crabs, dark crabs and even one with a black and white cross on its shell. Not a single one is green, so it's no wonder the kids eye me suspiciously when I tell them that these are all green shore crabs. Young crabs come in a vast array of colours, allowing them to blend in among the sand, seaweed and rocks. It's only as the crabs mature that they develop the classic olive-green mottled colour that gives them their name.

It's natural that the children all want to put their crabs in the big white tray of water I've set up, to show them off to their friends, but I have to say no. One of the reasons these crabs are so adaptable is that they will happily chew on anything, whether it's a passing periwinkle, a piece of bacon in a crabbing net or a fellow crab. Cannibalism is common among shore crabs, especially in overcrowded conditions. If we even put two or three of these crabs in a pot together they're likely to start fighting, or worse, so we choose just one crab to observe. I struggle with the sight of tourists crabbing on the quay each summer, the airless water in their buckets filled to the brim with a seething tangle of limbs. Rock pooling is a far more interesting and healthy experience for the children and for the crabs. We sit around the pool or the tray and watch a crab preening its gill covers and exploring its environment in peace.

Around one in ten children in the UK has never been to a beach and approximately half have never fished for crabs. Even for some children who live within easy walking distance of the seaside, my event for their school or club may be the only time in the year when they visit the beach. This is the first time some of these children have been in the rock pools, the only time they have seen a live crab face to face. No wonder it's a noisy encounter.

It doesn't take long for the children's curiosity to overcome their initial squeaks of terror. They begin trying to pick the crabs up with mixed success. They know to put a finger on the centre of its shell to hold it still, before grasping it gently under the armpits of its pincer legs using thumb and index finger, but no amount of careful explanation from me can prepare them for the feel of a live, moving animal in their hand. The crabs cycle their legs in the air, reaching back as far as they can, trying to free themselves. Even though it's impossible for these crabs to pinch the children's fingers if held correctly, the feel and the sight of the claws straining to reach their fingers triggers an instinctive reaction. Fortunately, we've also rehearsed holding the crabs low down, just over the water, so they can be safely dropped, avoiding casualties on both sides.

I'm certain that the love of this place and of these creatures begins here, in these screams and tumbling limbs, in these wide-eyed stares and dripping hands. It's all the better for taking the time to look, not just to count the crabs in and out, but to watch their mouths bubbling, to feel the tickle of hard legs scuttling across hands, to look into those alien stalked eyes and understand that these are living, breathing, eating, fighting masters of survival. Once the children experience these animals close up, I like to think that they won't want to cram dozens of crabs in a single bucket. Even more importantly, I hope they will take away with them a sense that the rock pools are a special place, somewhere that is a part of them. With so many pressures on the natural world, these young advocates are exactly what we need.

The green shore crab, on the other hand, is exactly what much of the world doesn't need. In its native range of Europe and North Africa it is very much part of the ecology, but it is easily transported elsewhere, especially when in its planktonic stage, by ships' ballast water, among shellfish catches and on the hulls of boats. Once green shore crabs arrive, there is no stopping them. The adult crabs can tolerate temperatures from freezing to over 30 degrees Celsius, water salinity from almost fresh to a concentrated brine, and they can survive for up to ten days out of the water in a damp place. As well as being happy to eat anything, including each other, they can make do without food for up to a month if needs must.

As exports go, this is a success story, with green shore crabs now established in places as far afield as North America, South America, South Africa and Australia. These new populations out-compete local species and have no hesitation in trying the local delicacies, especially the shellfish. Green shore crabs can crack open mussels with their claws and are especially fond of clams, so their impact on the North American soft clam fishery has been devastating. In the USA alone, they are estimated to cause around $22 million of damage every year. We have so many invasive marine species in the UK which affect our native ecology, from Pacific oysters and slipper limpets to sargassum seaweed and strange-looking skeleton shrimps, it's easy to assume that it's a one-way street. But the green shore crab is a reminder that any species introduced into a balanced ecosystem can cause damage in many unpredictable ways.

Invincible though they may seem, green shore crabs are a favourite meal of various fish and seabirds. Walking along the harbourside in Looe one sunny morning I watched a large male herring gull fly up from the muddy estuary with something large and wriggly in its beak. As I approached, he thudded down ahead of me and bashed a crab with a shell the size of my palm against the granite quayside a few times, before throwing his head back and gulping with his beak splayed wide open.

The crab threw its legs out wide and reached about with its pincers, flailing at the gull's face, bracing itself between the upper and lower beak. The contest carried on for another half-minute before one of the gull's shuddering attempts was successful and the crab, its legs still moving, plunged down the bird's gullet. Thick though the herring gull's neck was, the crab still created a considerable bulge.

I hope it was my imagination, but I was sure I could still see the crab moving as the gull swallowed again and again, pushing the lump towards its stomach.

Other times, I have seen gulls peck a crab shell clean and toss it aside, creating piles of discarded shells in their favourite eating places. When harassed by their thieving fellows, gulls will fly some distance carrying their catch to save their meal. This is how they come to drop crab shells in gardens far from the coast.

There is something else that can attack green shore crabs, something that seems rare on my local beaches, although it can be a common sight in other areas. To understand its method of attack, we need to take a look at crab reproduction, which again, in common with most sea creatures, is rather odd.

First of all, we have to locate the crab's tail, also known as the abdomen. If you are at all familiar with crabs, you'll know that they don't have an obvious tail. Unlike lobsters, prawns and crayfish, the crab doesn't carry its tail behind it, but keeps it neatly tucked under its bottom. This is one of the first things I look at with children at rock pooling events, because with a little practice it's easy to locate the tail and see whether a crab is male or female.

When you hold a crab upside down, the tail is clearly marked out as a flap which fits into a deep groove, forming either a small triangle or a wide arch shape. In females this is a large, curved area, which she can lift up and use to store her eggs. During the summer it's common to find female crabs with huge spongey clumps of yellow eggs held under their tails. The male crab, on the other hand, has no eggs to look after, so his tail is just a thin triangle shape.

It's not unusual to find two crabs together, one sitting on top of the other and grasping it tightly. The assumption is that the crabs are mating, which often causes older children to giggle and parents to offer evasive explanations to younger children. These are indeed mating pairs, but despite appearances they are not actually mating.

The crab on top is the male and he can tell from the chemical signals that the female is giving off that she is growing and will soon moult, shedding her entire outer shell. He has snatched her up and will carry her around for as long as it takes, which may be several days, during which he will try to fend off any other male crabs that show an interest. It doesn't look like much fun for the female to be held captive in this way, but the male knows that he can only mate with her when she has just moulted and her shell is soft. Crabs mate belly to belly, tail to tail.

Once mating is completed, the female will hide away while her shell hardens. Her clutch of eggs, once laid, stays safely under her tail until the larvae are ready to hatch out into the plankton. During this time the eggs change from a compact bright yellow patch to a spongey brown mass. The female then waits for the tide to rise, climbs to a high point with plenty of current, and stands erect on her back legs, rapidly flapping her tail to send the baby crabs out into the plankton.

It is this reproductive cycle that a parasitic barnacle uses to attack the green shore crab and take over its body. Perhaps I don't pay enough attention to shore crabs, given that they're so common on the shore, but it took me decades to see this barnacle for the first time and it was a child at an event who found it.

'It's a female,' he said, holding up his tub so I could see. 'I've learned about this. She's got eggs right there, under her tail.'

I picked her up to take a look. There was something there, a yellow, protruding lump. It was the colour of eggs and she was holding it like eggs, tucked under her tail and held in place by specialised grips, but this wasn't the usual soft egg-clutch I was expecting. It was hard, shiny and smooth. Normally I would be able to see the tiny eggs that make up the clump, but this was a single mass.

'It's a female, you're right,' I said, 'but she doesn't have eggs, it's something else.'

I was bursting with excitement, but the lad looked disappointed. 'They keep their eggs under there,' he said, 'I've read about it.'

A female green shore crab with a large clutch of eggs.

I reassured him that this was something even more exciting, if a little gruesome. He perked up at that thought.

The lump in question was the reproductive part of a *Sacculina carcini*, sometimes known as the crab hacker barnacle. It starts life swimming in the plankton, and its body shape at this stage is typical of a barnacle. When it is ready to parasitise a crab, it sheds its swimming legs and no longer looks anything like other crustaceans.

The crab's mouth, gills or other gaps in its armoury might seem the obvious ways in, but *Sacculina carcini* enters its host's body through the crab's antennae, latching on and injecting a tiny sac of its cells into the crab's bloodstream through a miniscule dart.

From this point on the crab is doomed. The barnacle spreads through the body of the host crab, creating a network of channels like roots. These allow it to draw in nutrients from the crab.

The effect of the parasite is obvious in the crab we've found. While the other crabs that children at my event have collected run about in their trays and buckets looking for things to eat or attack, the infected shore crab moves slowly, arthritically. The barnacle is sapping its energy as well as preventing the crab from naturally growing and moulting. This also means that it cannot repair damage by regrowing a lost claw with each moult as crabs usually do. The barnacle has taken over the crab's body. Less obvious, but perhaps most importantly, the parasitic barnacle has taken over the crab's mind.

Like all things in nature, the *Sacculina carcini* barnacle is intent on reproducing and it has a particularly cunning plan to convince the crab that it is pregnant, replacing the crab's eggs with its own and forcing the crab to care for them. The barnacle doesn't care whether it has infected a female crab or a male. If the crab is male, it simply changes the crab's hormonal balance, flattening the animal's abdomen to make its anatomy more female and

The parasitic barnacle *Sacculina carcini* is visible under the tail of this green shore crab.

controlling it to behave like a female. Once the barnacle has spread through the crab's body it begins to build its reproductive body exactly where the crab would naturally carry eggs: under its tail.

We could see this 'fruiting' body under our crab's tail: thick and lumpy like a tumour, with the developing larvae of the *Sacculina carcini* inside. Regardless of whether the carrier crab is male or female, when the time comes the host will know what to do. Just as it does instinctively with its own young, the infected crab heads for a high place exposed to the current, stands up and flaps its abdomen, stirring the water with a claw to ensure that the young are dispersed into the plankton, sending out a whole new generation of barnacles to parasitise other shore crabs.

As so often happens, I am fascinated and horrified in equal measure at seeing this creature. The parasitic barnacle is the one thing the resourceful green shore crab cannot hope to battle or evade. It's sad to leave this crab in its hapless state, but the barnacle too is an incredible animal. Authorities in North America have considered trying to introduce *Sacculina carcini* to help control invasive shore crab populations, but so far have decided against it. The danger of releasing the parasitic barnacle, as the arrival of the shore crabs themselves has proved, is that it is impossible to predict the impact of a newcomer to an ecosystem until it's too late to reverse it. Sometimes, you have to let nature pursue its own plan.

CHAPTER 8

Toothed Top Shell and Flat Periwinkle

I climb on a chair, open the door of the cupboard that hangs over the desk and lift down a cardboard box. It's surprisingly heavy and dust flies up, sparkling in the sunlight that streams through the window. The box makes a satisfying clatter when I set it down on the floor of my old bedroom and some sand slips out of a worn corner onto the carpet. Opening this box is like unwrapping my childhood. There's no special decoration, no protective covering and inside is a jumble of shells, large and small of all different colours and thicknesses, with no order or purpose; each one a treasure, collected on beaches from the Isles of Scilly to the Isle of Skye. Among them are limpets, mussels, and all sorts of large clams like razor and otter shells, shells I deigned special enough to go into the box: not everything made the cut. There's the small edible sea urchin I found on the Isles of Scilly and the large one I bought from a fisherman on the west coast of Scotland, which I would get out regularly to admire. I remember them all.

My biggest treasures are the smallest shells, which have settled to the bottom of the box. I unpack them last; hundreds of top shells and flat periwinkles, a molluscan rainbow of whites, yellows, pinks, purples, oranges, browns and blacks. I take some and run them under the water in the sink, just as I used to. As soon as they are wet, their colours intensify. I arrange them on the floor in no particular order. There is a simple pleasure in these empty shells that glow like jewels, and it is a joy I share with many children and adults who slip a seashell in their pocket before they leave a beach.

It is easy to tell flat periwinkles and top shells apart. Many marine snail shells extend into a pointed cone shape known as a spire. The flat periwinkles have almost no spire, as though their point has been sliced off. Their flattened top gives them an insular, secretive look, although their colours are bold. The top shells mostly have a rounded or pointed spire and have more obvious, bulging whorls, but the best and most rewarding way to recognise a top shell is to turn it upside down. The opening of a flat periwinkle, or almost any other sea snail shell, looks an

Topshells have a mother-of-pearl lining to their shell, as shown in this painted topshell.

Toothed Top Shell and Flat Periwinkle

opaque white or brown. The inside of a top shell glimmers and in the light it shines in sparkling pastel shades of pink and blue. This mother-of-pearl interior captivates me and everyone I show it to. In some shells it is more pronounced than others, but all of the top shells have it.

I've always imagined that one day I might use these shells for something, some great art work perhaps, or jewellery, or I might press the lot of them into drying cement to decorate a wall as some seaside houses have done. I will never see it through; I like these shells too much as they are. Even now I line my windowsills with shells that I have no idea what to do with, though these days I know far more about the animals that inhabited the shells than I ever used to when I first found them. Today, after picking out a few specimens I need for teaching a workshop, my collection is lovingly gathered up once more and the box returned to the cupboard of my childhood bedroom.

Many shores have lines of shells tumbled along the seabed and dumped by slowing waves as they hit the beach. I'm always drawn to these mixed up shells; they give an excellent idea of the sort of beach I'm on and the processes and ecosystems happening beneath the waves. Where the seabed is still and muddy there will be clam shells of all types, and on wind and wave-battered shores there are often mussels. The top shells and flat periwinkles I liked to collect occur almost anywhere with rocks and seaweed, especially more sheltered shores, where they can lie so thick on the beach that you almost wade through them to reach the pools – just like my local beaches where I now live in Looe, in South East Cornwall. There are piles of dead shells on my nearest beach and piles of living shells among the rocks and shallow pools. Limpets, of course, are everywhere, but the top shells and flat periwinkles are just as abundant.

The best adapted of all these snail shells to living at the top of the shore is the toothed or thick top shell, *Phorcus lineatus*. It enjoys the lack of competition on rocks exposed to high temperatures, air and variable salt and oxygen levels – it is so well adapted that it is never found below the midshore. The only thing it doesn't like is cold, so in the UK it is mainly a southerly species and populations can be wiped out by particularly cold winters. Some of the other top shells are more classically beautiful, with colourful markings and sculpted shapes, but this mollusc has a job to do and that job is surviving.

It would be unfair to suggest that the toothed top shell isn't attractive in its own way. It's something of a classic pear-shaped shell with a wide, sturdy bottom. All around the thick shell are dark zigzag lines, as though it has been coloured in by a heavy-handed child. Living in depressions and deep cracks in rocks, these shells make the best of any shade available to combat the overwhelming drying forces of sun and wind. Toothed top shells are out of the water for several hours twice a day. Just like the

Toothed top shells sheltering together at low tide.

Toothed Top Shell and Flat Periwinkle

limpets, these animals need their thick shells to save themselves from desiccation. They can't clamp down onto the rock as strongly as limpets, however, because they only have a relatively small and less-developed foot to cling on with. The toothed top shell has developed its own neat trick to solve this problem. Instead of a large sucker, it has a specially reinforced super-strength front door, known as the operculum.

The operculum is an easy thing to observe if you find a toothed top shell moving about in a pool or crossing the rocks on a damp day. It's a trick that children love to see, perhaps because it helps them to understand the top shell as a living animal with special abilities rather than just an inanimate shell.

The body of the toothed top shell is basically a pink colour with a pair of antennae on its head, rather like a garden snail, but it also has a collection of long thin sensory tentacles around its foot, which help it to find its way and feel for food. As soon as you pluck the snail from its pool, those delicate, striped tentacles disappear, pulled back into the shell by the strong foot muscles. The rest of the snail's body retreats behind them. The last part of the foot to be pulled in is a thick, dry circle, patterned with swirly lines like a fingerprint: the operculum. The animal squeezes itself into the shell and flips its operculum up behind it like a trap door. Once it's wiggled into position, this door provides a solid barrier to protect against predators and the elements. The door itself is hard and feels surprisingly dry for a part of a snail.

Once the operculum is fully closed, the other odd feature of the toothed top shell becomes evident: the 'tooth'. Of course, a snail has no use for an actual tooth. Like the limpets, these molluscs are equipped with a saw-like tongue, the radula, which they use to scour microalgae off the rocks. The 'tooth' is a triangular protrusion from the opening of the shell. What purpose it serves is a mystery, but presumably it gives the animal some advantage in this harsh environment. Perhaps it helps keep that vital operculum in place. None of the other top shells on the shore has a tooth. My efforts to enthuse children about the tooth fail to illicit much reaction, but the mother-of-pearl lining is always a hit and the shell is turned every which way to catch the sunlight until the child can be persuaded to part from it and return the top shell to its home.

Moving down the shore, we encounter more species of top shells, from the purple and the grey top shells that live almost anywhere on the shore, to the perfect cone of the painted top shells and the jelly-mould shape of the turban top shells, but it is almost always the toothed top shell that we meet first. At the end of rock pooling events, some of the children, and their parents, linger behind to walk the tideline, collecting empty top shells and periwinkles to take home – the start of a collection that may stay in a precious box, tucked away for the next generation to discover.

If you go rock pooling anywhere in northern Europe at any time of year, you stand a good chance of being rained upon. Most people clear the beach as soon as the heavens open and that's understandable, but nevertheless it's a shame. Rock pool animals aren't put off by precipitation, whether it's mist, mizzle, drizzle, showers, rain, downpour or deluge. This is their signal to emerge. With a much-reduced risk of drying out, lots of animals become far more active in wet weather than they would dare to be otherwise. This is the ideal time to go flat periwinkle watching.

As everyone else has gone home because of the rain, there's no need to worry about looks either. I go the whole hog and put on my waterproof overtrousers.

Pick any rocky beach with plenty of brown seaweeds like bladderwrack, egg wrack and serrated wrack on the upper to midshore and there will probably be some flat periwinkles crawling about. Despite their bright colours, flat periwinkles are often hard to spot; their yellows, oranges, browns and whites blending in among the seaweeds, sponges and rocks. The variation in colour seems to work in their favour, making them less obvious as you scan the tangled fronds of seaweed. Some flat periwinkles even mix up the colours, sporting stripes or chequerboard patterns of different yellows, oranges and browns.

These pretty animals don't mind too much where they are, how exposed the rocks are or whether the salinity is high or low. While limpets prefer to eat tiny microalgae that coat the rocks or very young seaweed growth, flat periwinkles graze on the big stuff. Wherever there are wracks to eat, they are happy. They're also quite fond of pepper dulse, a diminutive seaweed which gives off a spicy peppery smell if you crumble its flat fronds between your fingers. When the weather is dry flat periwinkles hide away under the mass of seaweed, but on damp days they are out and about.

The snail itself is far prettier than your average garden snail, with a slim creamy-orange translucent body tipped with a pair

A flat periwinkle on the move on egg wrack.

of broad-based tentacles. Instead of having eyes on the end of those sensory tentacles, the eyes are at the base. Between the two tentacles is a wide tubular mouth tinged with pink, which works like a nibbling hoover nozzle, scouring and sucking the seaweed. They are mesmerising to watch as they edge their way along, feeding through their vacuum attachments and flicking their head tentacles up and down, in a cancan-style dance.

There are two species of flat periwinkle, *Littorina fabalis* and *Littorina obtusata*. Both can occur on the same beach. Some books suggest that it's possible to look at the shape of the shell's flat spire or of its opening to determine the species, but whenever studies have been done they have found that this leads to lots of mistakes. There is only one way to know for sure which species you have, and that is to take an uncomfortably close look at the animal's penis. It's not as difficult as it sounds and doesn't involve molesting or injuring the snail in any way, but it has its challenges, especially when you're crawling about in the soggy seaweed in the rain.

It's hard to miss the male flat periwinkle's penis when the animal is sticking its head and body out of its shell to graze. The penis starts just behind the head and points back some distance along the side of the body, extending a similar length to the animal's head tentacles only much broader. Working out measurements can be tricky as the snail will instinctively retract into its shell when you approach it too closely with a camera or ruler. Once the animal is in position, you need to look at the arrangement of the knobbly glands along the side of its penis, and the shape and relative length of the smooth filament at the end of the penis. *L. fabalis* has a single row of glands and a longer filament, whereas *L. obtusata* has two rows of glands and a shorter filament. If you haven't given up by this point – and you probably should – you can use these penis observations to identify several individuals of each species, and you may be able to determine physical differences in the shape of their shells. Once you've done this, you can use the shell shape instead of penis examination to distinguish the two species, but only on that beach. If you go to a different beach you must go through the whole process again because the shape of flat periwinkles' shells varies between locations.

As all of this is time-consuming and staring at penises can feel a bit weird, I tend to assume it's not possible to know which *Littorina* species I've found.

Some other periwinkle species are even more tolerant of extremes than the flat periwinkle. Its smaller relative, the rough periwinkle, tolerates life higher up, even in the splash zone, where the tides only rarely cover the rocks and temperatures can soar on sunny days, choosing to hide in cracks in the rock and in the empty tests of acorn barnacles. Consequently, most visitors to the seaside will rarely notice these tiny snails, appreciate their incredible powers of survival or see how lovely they are. Rough periwinkles vary in colour in a similar way to the flat periwinkle, but have a sharply pointed shell. There has long been debate over whether there are many species of rough periwinkle or just different colour varieties. None of my identification books agree on the answer. Now that genetic testing is being applied to more marine species, we are starting to discover all sorts of things about them, and mysteries like these may be cleared up.

The more familiar common periwinkle, *Littorina littorea*, is brown and thick shelled. It's also known as the edible winkle and is still served up on the end of a pin in some places, although few of those eating them would realise what remarkable animals they are. Winkles congregate in huge numbers in warm, shallow pools near the top of the shore. Although they cannot live as high on the rocks as the rough periwinkle, they seem able to cope with extremely low oxygen levels that would kill most other marine animals.

Winkles often fall foul of large-scale shellfish gatherers, who can clear whole swathes of beach of these snails. Some operate within local licensing arrangements, but some do not. Removing part of the ecosystem wholesale evidently has an impact. The algae can grow faster, the hermit crabs find it harder to locate empty shells to use as homes and a food supply for larger animals like fish and starfish is no longer available. Just like fish stocks at sea, shellfish populations need to be sustainably managed.

Molluscs, like the winkle, the flat periwinkle and the toothed top shell, are the survival experts of the upper reaches of the rock pools. They may be inconspicuous and seem dull to the untrained eye, but their lives are far from uninteresting. They not only operate, but thrive here, at the edge of what is possible for life, taking extreme highs and lows of temperature, salinity and oxygen in their stride and using these challenges to their advantage. They are the tip of the marine iceberg, part of a vast, interconnected ocean of life, and this link to an altogether alien environment, together with their undeniable beauty, draws us to admire and collect their shells.

So far, we have only dipped a toe in the rock pools, into this world where everything about the way of life is beyond our experience. Deeper pools beckon.

PART TWO

ROCK POOL SPECIALISTS
The Middle Intertidal Zone

I often go on holiday to places that look just like home, with rugged coast lines, sheltered coves and place names in familiar-sounding Breton, Welsh or other Celtic languages. It goes without saying that all these places have particularly good rock pools, but on holiday we're unlikely to be organised enough to turn up at the beach at the right time or even to pick a period with good low tides, so I make the most of what I can access, which is often the middle shore.

Just such a holiday finds us pedalling along the Quiberon peninsula in southern Brittany. In typical holiday style I'm not sure what time the low tide will be, or even what time it is now, but the sun is high, using up the last of its late summer strength to warm the white sands that fringe this long spit of land. Swallows are flying low and congregating on the wires, preparing to race home to Africa ahead of the coming autumn storms, which will no doubt catch us on our return ferry journey. We freewheel the last stretch to the nearest beach, full of the joy that the absence of hills brings to inexperienced cyclists. We chain our bikes and rush down the granite steps to the sparkling sand.

One end of the beach is fringed with low dunes and a dark regiment of pine trees, the other is bright and open, ending in an outcrop of long rocky ridges like outstretched legs sitting in the water, letting the gentle waves lap their toes. Loose rocks will be gathered between these granite limbs and pools will have formed. I can't help but investigate.

The tide is half out, or half in. I'm not sure, but either way I'm an optimist. I see the rocks as an invitation to explore. This is not the seabed; these pools are exposed twice every day no matter how big or small the tide, and the creatures that live here are specialists, able to cope with warming sun, changing salinity and oxygen levels, and all the other pressures and changes of shore life. There are limpets, barnacles and shore crabs here, but also other rock pool animals that would not tolerate the extremes of the most exposed pools.

I keep my shoes on to save my feet on the slippery rocks, so I crouch at the edge of pools, leaning in as far as I dare, casting a shadow over the dense tangle of multicoloured seaweeds to watch blennies and gobies dart under boulders. Beneath a rounded stone glittering with quartz and mica I discover a pile of periwinkles and top shells, unmoving at first, but with the telltale antennae of hermit crabs poking out. Brittle stars, half-buried in the sand, sway along on feathered arms, and wherever there is a deeper hole or overhang, the rocks are coated in sulphurous sponges and mats of sea squirts.

A crab with an olive carapace slips out from beneath some seaweed and races for the shelter of a rock. I almost let it go. Shore crabs are so plentiful it's unnecessary to look at every last one, but something about this crab is odd. I think it is the eyes. They're too far apart. I lift it into an empty Pacific oyster shell filled with water to examine it and nearly fall over with excitement. This crab should be living further south along the Atlantic coast and Mediterranean, but it is migrating ever-northwards. I spend so much time looking at crabs that I hardly ever meet a new species, but this crab's rectangular shell with the eyes fixed at the corners of the widest edge is unlike any I've seen before. I have to convey it in its oyster carriage back over the rocky outcrop, across the slippery boulders, over the expanse of soft white sand to find a camera. I capture my first shot of a *Pachygrapsus marmoratus* rock crab on my other half's camera phone, taking in its dark wrinkled colouration, obscenely hairy legs and the four humps on the front of its shell, like a camel gone wrong, before I trek all the way back to release it.

As it side-steps its way under a rock, the tide is already rising, sending frothing surges of water through the channel between the outcrops, forcing me further back from the edge of the pool to save my trainers. The bubbling water brings vital oxygen and, as I watch, anemones begin to unfurl their tentacles and colourful purple and Pennant's top shells swivel from side to side, testing the cool water with their tentacles. These are creatures of routine, comfortable in their ever-changing world.

This is the middle-shore, where the pools are crammed with the classic and familiar rock pool species that illustrate every child's seashore book, but also some surprises. It is rich and varied, a homely place to those that inhabit it, but treacherous to any deeper-sea animal that becomes stranded here.

CHAPTER 9

Cushion Star

A visit to the rock pools never feels complete without a starfish. These animals are echinoderms, meaning 'spiny skins'. They are top of the list of creatures that people hope to find when they first go rock pooling, and they appear on every illustration of a rock pool I've ever seen. The iconic bright orange common starfish with five elegant arms can be found on the midshore but, despite its name, it is not the most common species, preferring slightly deeper waters. However, its smaller cousin, the cushion star, *Asterina gibbosa*, is a rock pool specialist.

A love for nature is often formed in childhood experience, when curiosity knows no bounds and life is lived through small adventures. Whatever we know best becomes our passion. For my mother, growing up in London, her passion was the trees and flowers of the parks, and the butterflies and hedgerow birds that lived in them. For me, growing up on the coast, in a world of wild open spaces and curved horizons, it was impossible not to be drawn to the seemingly more adventurous and mysterious lives that played out around me. The headlong dives of gannets, the ever-present risk of stepping on a sun-bathing adder and the fascination of finding an alien-looking starfish all captured my imagination. My mother also enjoyed all those things, but still tried to convince me that city wildlife could be worthwhile too. I was sceptical that anything exciting could exist in the confines of a London park. Being sure of myself as only children have the confidence to be, I never hesitated to pour scorn on that safe, urbane world of bird feeders and tame foxes that my mother remembered with such fondness.

I was wrong, of course. It was only as a grown-up when I moved to London to begin work in the Civil Service, after finishing my modern language studies, that I began to see things differently. I circled all the green patches on my *London A-Z* maps, picked out all the small ads for flats that were within walking distance of these parks and struck lucky by teaming up with a friend to make the move affordable. I came to appreciate the resilience and diversity of the wildlife that sprang up wherever it was given a chance. If I made an effort, I could find reed beds sparkling with damselflies and grass snakes rippling across pools. If I didn't try hard, I could always see foxes. In the countryside you never get to watch a vixen suckle her cubs outside your bedroom window. London even had some familiar sights, like cormorants slinking away underwater and black-headed gulls tumbling in shrieking masses over fish heading upstream to spawn.

Despite the gulf between my childhood experiences in Cornwall and those of my mother in post-war London, there are many things that we share. We have the same features, the same mannerisms and, far more importantly, the same passion for nature. Every time we see an unusual caterpillar or bird, we still rush into the house to look it up in our nature books and we sometimes stare into rock pools together. These moments of connection have always brought us together, but perhaps we have both come to recognise them as more precious since she fell ill with cancer. For a while, we couldn't be sure if we'd ever share such moments again. Life takes on new meaning when you come close to losing it.

Over the years, my mother coped admirably with my burgeoning shell collection and even today she tolerates my propensity to cover the breakfast table with trays, Petri dishes, microscopes and buckets of sea water. I'm not sure she finds all of the creatures as exciting as I do, but we both love cushion stars.

To live up to their picture book image, cushion stars are best seen on a sunny day, on a beach surrounded by turquoise seas and where the water is so clear you can step in a pool without realising it's there. If you can find an angle without too much reflection, you can watch the starfish going about their lives and feel that you are in there with them. On just such a day, around the time Mum was finally given the all clear after her cancer treatment, we found ourselves on Castle Beach in Falmouth, trying out my new camera in some midshore pools.

With the high season still a month away, the beach had an early morning sleepy feel, even though it was past midday. A man with a hammer was in the final stages of rebuilding the café after the winter storms, an unflinching elderly woman in a black swimming costume was shuffling through the breaking waves, trailing her hands in the bubbling water. A young mother followed her spade-waving toddler across the sand and my own son was demonstrating his fort-building skills to his grandad, pausing now and then to stare out from under his hat at the arc of the bay and the ominous container ships that were shoaling offshore.

The tide was dropping and we followed its foaming edge as it revealed new pools, talking about family or tomatoes or whatever other common experiences we could latch on to. By peering under overhangs and boulders it didn't take long to find our first cushion star. For Mum this evoked not her own childhood, but that of the children in her primary school classes, the thrill they felt at splashing through the cool pools while the rest of the school were back at their desks, the shouts of excitement when they found their first starfish, which was almost always a cushion star.

Although the animal itself is a pale green colour, it looks orange to our eyes. This is because its back is obscured by the orange splodges created by miniscule rings of spines that act like pincers, so tightly packed that we can barely see through them. These curved spines, known as pedicellariae, are the reason you never see starfish with algae growing on them.

Starfish always appear immaculately clean, whereas other intertidal animals like crabs that haven't moulted for a while are frequently encrusted with spiral worms. Limpets are often so plastered in wildlife that they are indistinguishable from the fauna covering the rocks around them. To avoid this, the starfish uses its pedicellariae to pluck off anything that tries to settle. The cushion star's puffy back and the contours of its five stubby arms are thoroughly coated in pedicellariae, giving it complete coverage to remove any life that attempts to colonise it.

Despite its warm amber colour, the starfish blends in well among the seaweeds and sponges of the pool. It looks unmoving and decorative, as though it belongs more on a Christmas tree than on the rock, so it is surprising, like glimpsing a trick of the light, when this stiff-bodied star begins to move. Its arms are still rigid, nothing seems to be happening, and yet it is disappearing over the edge of the rock. Wave-like, it glides in one smooth motion, surfing across the pink-paint seaweed, propelled by hundreds of translucent tentacle-feet that we can see reaching out from under its armpits, testing the way ahead.

When I pick it up and place it upside down in Mum's palm, those feet unfurl and sway, as fluid as a barley field on a windy day, creating swirling patterns that form and dissolve. Each tentacle has a swelling on the end, like a pale head of corn, which can sucker on to any surface. We turn the cushion star the right way up and the tentacle feet stick to Mum's hand. We place the animal back in the pool, our fingers connecting and parting as I coax the cushion star to let go, and we release this life back into its alien world.

Like many sea creatures, so different from any we meet in the terrestrial world, starfish stretch our powers of empathy. When it is motionless on the rock, I struggle to understand it as a fellow animal, but when it moves there is no doubt that it is a sentient being. The connection we feel is brief and one-sided. The starfish has its own path.

I remember how easily I left home to pursue my own interests and wonder if I have ever understood my parents or if my son will ever understand me. In the distance he is still there, shovelling sand, lost in his playful work. As soon as the cushion star feels the familiar rock beneath it, it wastes no time in seeking out food and shelter. We watch it slide off, slipping away from us, over a boulder and out of view.

Not all cushion stars look as perfect as the one my mum and I found. Many are more of a dull brown than a bright orange and, although the books will tell you they have five arms, it seems they aren't good at counting. I have found cushion stars with as few as two arms, others with three or four, and one that was trying to pass for a seven-armed starfish.

Cushion stars, like other starfish, possess incredible powers of regeneration, and it is one of the strangest things to witness on the shore. There's a story I've often heard recounted, although I've never found any evidence for it. It may have happened in Scotland, Ireland, France or the USA, depending on who is telling it, and it changes at every retelling.

The favourite food of most starfish is shellfish, things like mussels and oysters, that people also like to eat. Inevitably, the fishing community often see starfish as a pest, especially if they are farming or fishing shellfish for a living and experience starfish attacking their beds. According to the story, when this happened to one group of fishermen, they did what any practical type would do and made use of whatever came to hand, which in the case of fishermen tends to be a gutting knife. It became standard practice to pick some of the starfish out of the haul, slash them in half and throw their corpses into the sea. The fishermen did this over and over, and more and more frequently, because the number of starfish seemed to increase despite their efforts. In response, they stepped it up, making sure every starfish was chopped in half and thrown overboard. As time went by, the starfish became an epidemic. By the time they realised what was wrong, the fishery was overrun with starfish. It turned out that they had been inadvertently doubling the population. When they

This damaged cushion star has lost one arm and regrown three new ones in its place.

threw the two halves of the starfish back in, each half regrew into a new starfish, eager to chomp on the shellfish.

This might be an exaggeration, but there is some truth in this story. The ability of a starfish to grow new limbs is legendary, although it is not unlimited. A starfish must have at least part of its central disc attached if it is going to grow new arms, so a single arm without the disc could not turn into a new starfish and would die. However, if the animal has been split in a way that leaves a working part of the central disc attached to one or more severed arms, then the separated part may regrow into a complete new animal. Some starfish species are even known to be able to deliberately divide themselves in two as a quick means of reproduction, and some Hawaiian starfish species can intentionally shed a single arm which grows into a new starfish.

The mutant cushion stars I find on the shore have not been attacked by misguided shellfish growers but have lost limbs in encounters with predators or accidents. The regeneration process is not a fast one, so there is sometimes no outward sign that a four-armed cushion star was not born that way, but more often the new arms are clearly growing. Sometimes there are minute stumps sticking out of the animal's side, other times there is just a subtle difference in the length of the arms that indicates some are still in the process of regrowing. And occasionally a cushion star is so carried away in its efforts to regrow limbs that it ends up with more than five. These incredible powers of regeneration are of interest to medical scientists, who hope to discover secrets that might be of use in humans one day.

At the other end of the scale from the diminutive cushion stars, spiny starfish have long arms and can measure up to 70 centimetres from arm-tip to arm-tip. Most people hesitate to pick them up due to their fearsome-looking armour-plating of thick white or purple-tipped spines. Although some young spiny starfish are red or brown, they often develop a striking blue or mauve tinge as they grow, making their outline stand out from the seabed when they glide over sand, although often they are so well wedged into a rocky crevice that only the tips of a couple of arms are visible. Despite their size and prickly appearance, spiny starfish are completely harmless to us.

One thing that children are quick to notice is that the starfish's mouth, found dead-centre on its underside, is its only orifice. Just like anemones, everything goes in and out of the same hole. This is enough information for most people, but, in the name of science, an explanation is needed of just how an animal with no teeth, no claws and just a tiny mouth-bottom can feed. In the case of the cushion star, which specialises in hoovering up microscopic organisms and other detritus, the feeding strategy is simply to suck everything in, but its larger relatives like the spiny starfish have far less delicate table manners.

My son delights in finding feeding starfish; having heard the details many times he recognises without hesitation when an animal is mid-meal. They're especially easy to see at our local aquarium, where the lack of natural hideaways and the availability of food result in there always being at least one starfish eating. Even from a distance it's obvious there's something happening; the starfish looks deformed, its long arms drawn in, its central disc pushed up. It's an awkward-looking stance, roughly how I must look when my nieces force me to try out the 'crab' position they've learned in gym class, with my hands under my head and belly to the sky. Although it can feel all too strenuous, holding myself in a weird pose is nothing like as demanding as what the starfish has to do.

My boy finds a starfish on our local beach that has grasped a sting winkle. It has levered itself into an arched handstand with

Common starfish with its stomach pushed out, eating a netted dog whelk.

just the tip of the sting winkle's spire protruding from between its armpits. It's a plain, muddy-coloured starfish, not the sort I'd normally rush to grab the camera for, but my son wants me to capture all the gory details.

A starfish meal can last many hours, and we only have a few minutes before the tide will return, but it's enough to get the gist of what's going on. We prise the starfish from the rock and turn it over. Underneath, its tentacles are working hard, securing the hapless snail in place by the head with the assistance of dozens of sticky suckers. The starfish's mouth has disappeared, enveloped in a pale mass that is smothering most of the body of the sting winkle.

'That's the stomach,' my lad says, with far too much pleasure. I nod and we both stare at the winkle's half-consumed body, unable to take our eyes off it.

The starfish has extruded its stomach through its mouth to engulf its prey. Before it can reabsorb its stomach and meal, it must marinade the sting winkle's soft parts in its digestive juices.

This might take a while, but the starfish has all day. It has to be especially patient with its favourite food of bivalves: shells that have two halves, like mussels and cockles. These shells are able to clamp shut using their strong muscles when the starfish attacks. With its raised, protective position, the starfish stops predators stealing its prey and exerts as much force as it can by pulling the two sides of the clam shell apart with its arms. A war of attrition begins, which can take many hours, but eventually the bivalve will weaken and the starfish is able to push its stomach into the gaping shell to begin digestion. Just an empty shell is left behind.

There is no equivalent of the starfish on land. They and their cousins, the sea urchins, brittle stars, feather stars and sea cucumbers, are all exclusively marine animals; strange and exotically attractive to us bipeds in their radial symmetry and spiny skin. The regenerating limbs and alien eating habits of starfish only add to the fascination.

CHAPTER 10

Velvet Swimming Crab

Everyone has to be afraid of something, and my personal phobia is that someone will rock up at the shore laboratory with a massive velvet swimming crab at the bottom of their bucket. It's a fear I regularly live out, knowing that whoever finds it will ask me to pick it up for them.

I want to say no, but when all the expectant faces crowd around, I find myself squaring up with an animal that most definitely will not want to be held.

The shore laboratory is at the heart of any group rock pooling event and fulfils several important functions. This collection of water-filled buckets and trays is where new finds are brought to be observed and identified. Keeping the animals safe is always the priority on the shore, so only one of each species found is added to the laboratory, allowing most animals to be returned promptly to their pools. The laboratory becomes a diverse collection, giving all participants the chance to see a range of species up close and, most importantly of all, to take time to observe them and learn about their lives. In a tray, we might have a spiny starfish, a cushion star, some hermit crabs, top shells and a blenny and they will all get along, no problem.

However, when someone brings in a velvet swimming crab, there's no question of it going in the tray. The result could be carnage. Even small ones require their own tray or bucket.

When there is a tiny juvenile velvet swimming crab in a shallow tray, where I can grab it quickly, I will sometimes pick it up to show, but I'd rather people admire its beauty in situ or move along to looking at the giant spiny starfish in the tray next door. With larger crabs I prefer to use a long stick – a kelp stipe is perfect – to point out some key features while maintaining a good distance. If I need to pick the crab up, I usually scoop it into a large tub, rather than trying to grab it with my bare hands.

I once let a courageous member of the public have the privilege of showing a velvet swimmer round the group. He could see I didn't want to go near it and stepped in, full of confidence, saying crabs didn't bother him. Five seconds later, the wriggling velvet swimming crab had secured a hold on his thumb. Everyone around him leaped away shrieking and the look on his face suggested that he would never pick up another crab that wasn't in a sandwich as long as he lived.

I know I should have come forward and expertly prised the crab's pincers from the man's blanched digit. With a different crab I might have risked it. Instead, I picked up a large bucket and held it at arm's length underneath the crab, which was spinning its back legs and lurching from side to side. After the initial commotion, silence had fallen over the onlookers, punctuated by the odd gasp as the crab and the man carried on their awkward dance. It probably only lasted a few seconds, but it felt longer to me and probably longer still to the man. Somehow the crab dislodged itself, tumbled into the bucket with a plop and swam down into the water, leaving the man's muttered curses behind. Although fully grown crabs may have pincers powerful enough to do some damage to a human finger bone, this one only left a red mark and wounded pride. The crab was released and

Velvet swimming crab.

a lesson learned: never to put fingers anywhere near a velvet swimming crab.

Every regular rock pooler I've ever met agrees with me, though some are braver. My son calls this animal the devil crab, and he's not alone. It's best to be cautious and gentle with all wild animals, but this one demands even more respect.

My fear of handling velvet swimming crabs in no way means that I don't like them. Yes, their preferred means of introduction is to rear up on their hind legs with their pincers aloft, but only if you disturb them. If you're close enough to discover that their backs are covered in a dense coat of soft, velvety hairs, you are too close. For all that velour, there is nothing cuddly about them. As I prefer not to invade their personal space, most of my encounters with velvet swimming crabs are calm affairs that don't involve a screaming crowd or any animosity. When watched from a distance, these crabs are some of the most exciting on the shore. The secret, as always, is to take things slowly.

I like to look for velvet swimming crabs in the winter. They're about all year, but on a quiet, undisturbed beach, when all the summer growth of seaweed has died back, there's a better chance of spotting these secretive animals.

My tolerance of the cold is well below average and beach trips in the winter months require three pairs of boot socks inside my wellies, several warm layers and full head-to-toe waterproofs. By the time I'm ready on this dark January morning I can barely move, and I look as though I have eaten more than my fair share of Christmas pudding. It's a good thing I don't have far to walk to my nearest beach.

The sky moves in at this time of year, ponderous grey clouds hang low over Rame Head, chided along by the blustery wind and if it's not already raining it's about to. Half-rainbows flare into life over land and sea, and the shore knuckles down to surviving a different set of challenges as storms pummel in and floodwater surges out. The burning sun and turquoise waters of the summer are long gone, replaced by wind chill and white horses, the swell often rendering many of my favourite pools and gullies inaccessible. For all this turmoil, there is much to see on the midshore as the beach finally breathes in after the constraints of summer.

No one else stays on the beach as long as I do. I need to move slowly to gather photos for my blog, stopping for minutes at a time by each pool and staring into dark overhangs. A man walks a short distance on the sand, intermittently throwing a ball for an eager spaniel, but leaves when the next shower starts. As pulses of rain sweep across the beach, a grey heron flies down and perches on the rock, looking for fish exposed by the falling tide, its feathers ruffling backwards in the wind. The heron and I have the beach to ourselves.

I cross the first rocks to some sandy gullies, edging slowly through patches of deep water that threaten to engulf my wellies with freezing water, to a section littered with large boulders that is perfect for crabs.

The sand on the bed of the pool is a deep grey mix of slate, quartz and shells, coarse grained and liable to give way underfoot. I take a moment to wonder if there is quicksand on this beach, and whether I've remembered to put my phone in my bag. As I contemplate whether the lone heron might be the last thing to see me alive, my eyes scan the sand; the kaleidoscope of tiny grains in white, black, grey and red. I stare longer at the red spot and, sure enough, there is another one a few centimetres to the right. The eyes of a velvet swimming crab. When I look closer, a few of the jagged teeth on the front of its shell are also discernible. The rest of its body is hidden in the sand. I move a step nearer and it lifts its shell, the sand sliding off it into the pool to reveal blue-tinged pincers which it holds up in a demonstration of strength. It side-steps around me, fixing me with those blood-red eyes, before sending up a flurry of sand granules with its black and white striped rear legs, scooting through the water and away into the cover of some seaweed.

I pull some bladderwrack to one side to reveal a vertical fissure in the rock, at the base of which a male velvet swimming crab is clutching a female, waiting for her to moult. Close-up, I can see their stripy rear legs held up at an awkward angle behind them. The swimming legs are flattened so much they are almost paper thin and are fringed with long hairs, making them look even wider, like the tip of an oar. When the velvet swimming crab wants to make a quick getaway, it whirs these paddles, allowing it to swim quickly and with a lot of control. They also come in handy if anything attacks from above. When the crab adopts its classic standing position with its claws raised, it can flick its back legs and hop up, sometimes jumping out of the water, while snapping its long chopstick claws together. It's a ninja attack strategy which must look even more alarming to the crab's prey than it does to me, so I'm happy to watch from a distance, bringing my camera only as close as I dare.

The deep azure tinge to the claws is more striking close-up. Although these crabs appear black, the whole shell is blue beneath the dark layer of velvety fuzz. The mesmerising colours of the velvet swimming crab make it one of my favourite animals to watch. This is a skilled hunter, a merciless survivor and a truly beautiful animal. After a couple of hours I will be glad to leave this lonely beach and return to the warm, but this crab is perfectly equipped to overcome everything the winter will throw at it.

I have an uneasy relationship with the fishmonger; as a vegetarian who loves marine life, it's not my favoured hang-out. Yet I can't help myself. Whenever I see a fish counter I have to take a look, see what has been caught. Our local fishmonger's and others like them do a sterling job of trying to convince the public to sample a range of different species, and to promote those which are caught from relatively sustainable fisheries, but it's an uphill battle these days. Most fish selling outlets offer a limited choice and that is what most people buy. Whether it comes down to commercial good sense that the shops simply offer only the species that the public will buy, or whether the public buy only a few species because they haven't had the chance to try others, is hard to tell. In other countries a huge variety of fish and shellfish is on sale. It also interests me that in the UK, while several species of fish are on offer, only one species of crab is usually sold.

I feel sorry for *Cancer pagurus*, the edible crab, as it is most commonly known. The fishermen know it as brown crab and here in Cornwall some people call it the pasty crab, because it has an oval shell, smooth around the back and crimped like a pasty across the front. It's the crab that's sold in restaurants, in crab sandwiches and crab salads.

An edible crab hiding in a crevice.

Because of its name, the common assumption is that the edible crab is the only crab that you can eat, but this couldn't be further from the truth. All crabs are edible, although some species are too small to be commercially viable. Three are regularly fished in our waters: the edible crab, the spider crab and the velvet swimming crab.

Crab potting is a relatively sustainable fishery, which takes limited numbers of animals in a very targeted way using small boats and traditional methods. It's a tough job and in times of rough weather, when boats can't put to sea, there can be long stretches with no income. At least one of our local crab potters moonlights as a taxi driver.

Although the spider crab is fished in significant numbers, hardly any of these or the velvet swimming crabs are sold in the UK, the vast majority being exported live to France or Spain. Only the edible crab tends to be sold on the home market. The focus on a single species makes little sense and crab potters do their best to encourage a local market for other species, even offering spider crab tasting at local events. Perhaps it's time for those who choose to eat shellfish to be more adventurous in what they eat?

I often find large edible crabs on the lower shore and sometimes lobsters too, but if I post photos or videos on social media they inevitably provoke questions about the location and comments about putting them on a plate. As a naturalist, it is disheartening that my work to share the lives of these animals attracts the interest of those who would harm them. Some things are best kept quiet.

Although we inevitably come into conflict on occasion because so many decisions are made for short-term economic gain rather than sustainability, some of the goals of the fishing community and conservationists are not always so very different. Crabs take years to reach maturity and, although they can only be legally fished when their shell reaches a minimum size, the limit is only 14 centimetres in edible crabs. Mature crabs can reach around 25 centimetres, which means that some of the crabs that are caught are still relatively small and young. Keeping some large crabs secret means that they survive to reproduce and help renew the population. Securing stocks for fishing may not be conservationists' main motivation, but the work we do to monitor and protect the shores where these crabs grow up is an important part of maintaining a sustainable fishery.

I wonder though, if other people spent time watching crabs grooming and wiping their faces with their antennae, burying themselves in the sand to hide, using their claws like cutlery to dissect a meal, and staring back with their strange, stalked eyes, would they still feel the same about that crab sandwich? They'd probably still eat crab sandwiches, but perhaps with a greater respect for the incredible life of their filling. As with most things in life, respect is the key.

CHAPTER 11

Hermit Crab

Once a year, just before the summer holidays, I lead rock
pooling sessions for the local Beavers and Cubs packs. It's always
a noisy, chaotic affair when the pack is let loose on the beach,
releasing pent-up energy after a day in school. I start with the
Beavers, as a warm-up, acclimatising myself to their tumble
of energy and chatter, trying to keep up with their questions,
stories of fishing adventures and frantic toing and froing in their
search for crabs. They scurry back and forth among the pools,
hauling dripping buckets with them, and the shore laboratory
quickly accumulates finds, each child desperate for their own
haul of baby shore crabs to be included. I have to tread a fine
line between encouraging the children's enthusiasm and saving
the creatures from it. Soon, they stumble upon a pool packed
with hermit crabs and these too come in by the bucket load.
Fortunately, as they are rather more sociable than the velvet
swimming crabs, we can keep hermit crabs together without risk
of injury. The trays quickly become surrounded by the faces of
children, who kneel or lie as close as they can to watch the crabs
as they peep out of their shells and cautiously extend their long
legs and stalked eyes.

The hour with the Beavers goes quickly, in a whirl of blue polo shirts and woggles, but there's no time to rest. The eight- to ten-year-olds of my next group are already waiting for me at the top of the beach. It should be the same again but with green polo shirts instead of blue, however noise levels have increased exponentially with the children's size and these long-limbed kids are more confident, forming groups that stampede between pools and work together to attempt to move giant boulders and uncover crabs as big as their imaginations. Most of the Cubs know this beach well as they live in the area, and they all have things they plan to find, from basic crabs to sharks and octopuses. It is unfortunate that these evening sessions can never coincide with big low tides, which always happen around the middle of the day, so we can only access the upper and the middle shore.

The Scout leaders slip seamlessly from sharing in the children's excitement to reining in their potentially foot-crushing attempts to move enormous rocks. My son, who has taken some of the less confident children under his wing to help them find things, rushes over with something in a pot. He weaves his way through the crowd of boys who are showing me their crabs, of which we've quickly accumulated several species. He keeps finding his path blocked and, although it's hard to hear much over the shouts of the others, he's saying something about a hermit crab. There must be something special about it because he knows that we already have a whole community of hermit crabs exploring the confines of a tray, some emerging for a second before jumping back into their shells, others running around and tapping on any shells they might like to move into.

Eventually my son finds a gap to reach me, and he's out of breath from shouting out and trying to force his way through. He holds up his pot. In it is a white creature, curled in a spiral like the pattern of a snail shell. It looks like a worm out of its burrow at the

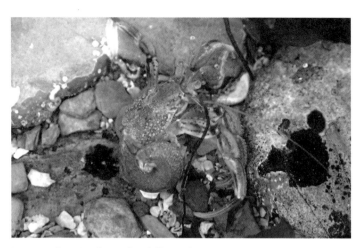

A common hermit crab out of its shell. *Jan Whittington*

back, but at the front it has the strong pincers, legs and yellow eyes of a hermit crab. My child opens his other hand to reveal a large painted top shell. He grins, knowing he's done the right thing.

'It was under a stone,' he says, nodding towards the hermit with the white bottom. 'I think it was trying to get into the top shell.' His friends confirm his account, clearly delighted.

One of the first things many children learn about rock pool animals is that hermit crabs don't have shells of their own and instead have to find marine snail shells to live in. That curly white bottom is soft and extremely vulnerable to predators but is perfectly shaped to hook around inside the internal structure of a shell, holding it securely in place as armour against predators. However, hermit crabs, like other crabs, grow throughout their lives and, as they do so, they moult their hard parts: shedding the outer shell of their claws, legs and even the shell of their stalked eyes, allowing their new and soft inner shell to expand and harden. Hermit crabs' curled bottoms also grow with them until they become too big for their shells. Sometimes they can be surprisingly co-operative about this process, pragmatically forming a queue from largest to smallest behind the biggest crab which has found an empty shell. They patiently await the magic moment. When the largest crab moves into the vacant shell, the next in line hops into the newly available shell and so on, in a domino chain, until the smallest hermit wedges its little curly tail into the last available shell, leaving its old home behind for some tiny crab to find. Other times, hermit crabs can be more brutal, fighting over the best shells. If a larger hermit wants a shell that's already occupied, it will try to dislodge the occupant and run off with its house.

As you might imagine, hermit crabs are neurotic about timing their house move just right. Whenever their soft parts are out of the shell and unprotected, they are liable to be eaten by other crabs, fish and other predators. Too much procrastination and another hermit crab will steal the shell. The hermit crab that my son found would have discovered its vacant painted top shell and checked it over carefully for flaws or for other occupants before moving it under a rock to create a secure changing room for its costume change. First placing the top shell in the correct orientation, it would then have shuffled itself into position and taken a last look around to check for marauding crabs, swivelling its eyes to take in a full 360-degree view. In an operation calculated to take just a few seconds, it unfurled its bottom from its old shell, swivelled it towards its new home and prepared to feel its soft bottom slide into the blissful comfort of its new abode. At this crucial juncture, it was struck by disaster when its rock was overturned, sending the top shell tumbling away in the current. As if that wasn't already bad enough, a boy in a green polo shirt then scooped it into an old margarine tub.

After an hour of tearing about the beach, the children have blown out some of their initial energy and we gather around the tray to examine the finds. I'm careful not to let go of the tub as

I show them the soft hermit crab caught short between shells. Poking, prying, grabbing fingers or a fall from the tub would be the end of it. These crabs are so quick at changing their shell that it's rare to have the chance to see them in this exposed state. When everyone has seen the naked hermit crab, Junior and I place the top shell in the tub alongside it. Its relief is evident. Within a minute the crab has sidled up to the top shell, wound its curly tail through the internal structure of the shell's twisting spire and lifted its new home firmly into place. Next time it changes its shell it will be even more careful.

Watching the children interacting with the animals, I find it interesting how some overcome their fears and have a go at holding starfish and crabs for the first time. It's not always the most timid children who are unsure of themselves. It sometimes seems harder for tougher kids who see themselves as leaders to take these risks. The stakes are higher if they fail. When they don't feel able to go near the bigger crabs, children can build up their confidence with the hermit crabs, which they can pick up by the borrowed snail shell without hurting themselves or the crab.

Another thing that happens all the time is that the child who doesn't think they're good at finding anything brings in the find of the day.

At the start of the Cubs session I notice a lad who seems to be on the edge of the groups that have formed. He sets off on his own, moving slowly and scuffing his feet on the rocks. The trainers he's wearing aren't the right shoes for going in the pools, so he watches the others from a distance as they wade, knee-deep in the water, chasing crabs. When they wave at him to come and help, he turns away and wanders further across a rocky outcrop before disappearing into a deep gully.

I'm wondering if I should break away from the Cubs that have gathered around me to check on this kid, when he reappears, pot in hand.

'It's just a hermit crab,' he says, 'I never find anything interesting.'

He makes to place it in the tray with the other hermits. There are already dozens of them in there, but I stop him and ask to take a look.

I can see straight away that this one is different, but initially he ignores my efforts to persuade him that it is something special. He's not keen on kindness. Other people have already found loads of hermit crabs so he seems sure I'm only trying to make him feel better. I insist that he looks closer with me and his jaw drops as it sinks in that this is a completely different hermit crab from all the others the Cubs have found. It's a great find and this particular species has a special story.

At the end of our hour everyone gathers to look at the finds before we return them to their pools. I ask the boy to show his special crab to the others. It is in a common periwinkle shell, like

St Piran's hermit crab.

so many of the others in the tray, and at first the other children don't see the difference. He points out the long antennae peeping out from under the edge of the shell, which are bright red, then we take turns to hold it close to our faces so that we can see the hermit crab's eyes properly. The children's faces light up the moment they manage to focus on the crab's eyes, which are black with white dots, as though it is looking out through a chess board or a star-studded night. The boy cups a hand underneath the hermit crab's shell as well as gripping it in the other hand. He snatches it back if any prying fingers seem to threaten it. His triumph has melded into something that is not just proprietorial. The crab has become his responsibility, his sole focus. This may be the first time he has connected in this way with a wild animal and discovered the wonder that comes with these unforced encounters with the natural world. Whether it comes from watching birds at a garden feeder, spotting a distant animal from a hide or holding a hermit crab in your hand, the feeling is intense and rewarding. This boy's connection is uniquely his.

I also pass round one of our common hermit crabs (which I like to call 'Bernards' after their scientific name, *Pagurus bernhardus*), so everyone can see its yellow eyes and the swollen right claw, used for breaking and for fighting, which is much larger than the left. Our starry-eyed crab has two claws about the same size, which is unusual in hermit crabs; perhaps it is a more peaceful species or it might prefer softer prey. Whatever the reason, these equal claws are unique among the British species. What the children like especially is that this little hermit has hairy legs.

After this equal-clawed hermit crab was shown to the nation on the BBC programme *Springwatch* in 2016, a common name was chosen for it by a public vote. St Piran's, the selected name, is a good fit for this hermit crab which, in the UK, is mostly found in Cornwall, where St Piran is the patron saint. The crab's eyes also resemble the colours of the Cornish flag: a black background representing the rock of the mines, with a white cross representing the tin. This crab was in particular need of an English name because its scientific name, *Clibanarius erythropus*, is especially unmemorable.

More of a southerly species, this hermit crab is common on beaches in Brittany and occurs in the Channel Islands, but has tended to be right at its limit in Cornwall and West Devon, where records of it have been patchy. It was first found in Cornwall at Mousehole by Dr Nick Tregenza in 1960. The hermit crab's larvae had probably arrived in Cornwall from Brittany in the plankton due to favourable warm conditions, and from 1960 onwards the crabs were regularly recorded by Alan J. and Eve C. Southward in several locations in Cornwall and in Wembury in Devon. In 1985 the St Piran's crab was recorded alive in Marazion, near Penzance, and in Wembury. After that it disappeared, with only dead crabs found, then none at all. It is likely that colder sea temperatures around this time meant that no new hermit crab larvae could settle on the shore, so the existing population died of natural causes. Other man-made pressures, however, could well have contributed to their demise. St Piran's crabs in the UK prefer to make their homes in dog whelk shells, which became scarcer around this time due to the effects of a chemical used in anti-fouling paints. It may also be no coincidence that these hermit crabs were not found alive on any Cornish beaches from 1967 until 1973. These were the beaches most severely affected in the 1967 *Torrey Canyon* oil disaster.

After 1985, there were no more sightings at all of the St Piran's crab in mainland UK until 2016, almost exactly 50 years after the *Torrey Canyon* disaster and 31 years after the last previous record. Adrian Rowlands, a volunteer taking part in Shoresearch in Falmouth, a Cornwall Wildlife Trust citizen science project, noticed a hermit crab in a tiny shell that looked a bit different. Its red antennae, equal claws and chequerboard eyes were unfamiliar to everyone on the beach, but it was soon confirmed as a new record of *Clibanarius erythropus*. Further sightings followed in Mousehole, where the hermit was first discovered, in Penzance and near Porthcothan on the north coast. This species of hermit crab seemed especially sociable, often found clustered together in shallow pools on the middle shore, among loose stones or even out of the water. Once volunteers around the county knew what to look for, new records came flooding in. The crabs were found in progressively larger shells, on more and more beaches, including at Wembury, which had been its last stronghold until 1985. This special little hermit crab was finally back in South West England and establishing itself.

Although the St Piran's crab's long-term survival on our shores may depend on sea temperatures being high enough to allow new larvae to survive in the plankton and successfully settle, for now the St Piran's crab is back, living alongside the common Bernards.

At the end of the rock pooling session, the Cubs return their finds, in the evening's last blast of shouting and splashing. I feel a pang watching the boy who had found the St Piran's crab making his way back to his hidden gulley to release his find, knowing the mixture of feelings that come in letting something special go, while setting it free. His joy at finding the crab cannot be dampened by parting though, and he is no longer dragging his feet. He rushes back to me, wobbling on the slippery rocks, his face split in a huge grin. He has exchanged his hermit crab for this latest find, a large piece of Victorian sewage pipe. He cheerfully lugs it homewards.

CHAPTER 12

Snakelocks Anemone

Through the blazing summer sun, the gentle mists of autumn, the boiling swells of winter and the mellow light of spring, I am never bored on the beach. My son, on the other hand, is more discerning. He's less tolerant of the horizontal rain, the hours of staring into seaweed and the endless summer events where he's expected to look at yet more shore crabs. We often reach a compromise so that he can dig dams and build rock forts at the top of the shore while I wander into the distance to look at creatures, only sharing the most exciting finds. When it comes to night rock pooling, however, no such compromises are necessary. The second I suggest an after-dark expedition, he rushes off to find his head torch and grab his wellies.

Most beaches are deserted at night and there's something surreptitious about walking there after dark. I always half expect the police or coastguard to turn up, alerted by someone looking out from behind a twitching curtain as strange lights move about on the beach. At first, a watcher might assume us to be anglers, who sometimes set up their rods on the rocks at night to catch bass and other fish that are active after dark. Instead they would see our torches moving back and forth along hidden gullies, popping up from behind rocks and disappearing again, sometimes turning off completely, to be replaced by a blueish glow. Smuggling still happens around our coasts, illegal fishing too. Quite what the police would make of a group of adults and children on the lower shore at midnight I don't know. So far, no one has called them, but I do know that this is the very best time to see the rock pools in action.

The sense of adventure is invigorating. From the moment we step outside and feel the chill night air on our cheeks we become explorers, alone in the night. Our footsteps in the sand are a bit louder, the sounds of humanity a bit fainter, as we move into the blackness of the unlit beach. Somewhere out there is the dark line of the sea. Sounds of wash and swash carry to our ears, but the dark water remains invisible to us as we cross the rocks, an ominous presence that will soon return to envelop everything. For my son and his friends, this is far more than an opportunity to legitimately stay up past bedtime. It is a step into the wild, into an unfamiliar nightscape where anything might be lurking unseen. We hold hands to steady ourselves on the slippery seaweed, blind each other as we look about with our head torches and stumble into rush hour in the rock pools – where prawns and fish swim in the open while crabs and hermit crabs bustle around their pools and even across the rocks at our feet. It's a great time to observe hermit crabs fighting over females, green shore crabs hunting for food and fish defending their territories. This is also the very best time to look at snakelocks anemones.

The snakelocks anemone, *Anemonia viridis*, is quite unlike any of our other intertidal anemones. Found from the midshore downwards, it's easy to see how its crown of long hair-like tentacles that swirl in the current resemble the snake locks of the Medusa. In many snakelocks anemones these tentacles are a vivid, reptilian green, with each tentacle tipped in purple, but five different colour morphs have been identified. Out of the water, the snakelocks anemone simply collapses, splaying its tentacles in an undignified heap as the tide retreats. Most other species of anemone retract their tentacles when they are out of the water, forming a neat wine-gum blob on the rock, but snakelocks anemones cannot do this and form these messy green splats, rather like a stranded jellyfish.

One of the many curious things about these anemones is that they contain tiny microalgae, known as zooxanthellae, which live inside snakelocks anemones' tentacles in varying concentrations. The anemones benefit from this symbiotic relationship by receiving energy in the form of sugars from the photosynthesising algae, while the algae benefit from the protection the stinging anemone offers from the many grazing molluscs that roam the shore. I wonder if the presence of these tiny algae could be the reason that this anemone can be found not just on rock, but living on fronds of kelp, other seaweeds and seagrass. From its elevated position among the seaweeds, the tentacles of the anemone are exposed to the sunlight, ensuring that the symbiotic algae can photosynthesise effectively. Unfortunately for swimmers and rock poolers, this also means that bare legs and arms are likely to brush against these dense clumps of tentacles, which can inflict a mild sting.

Increased levels of carbon dioxide in the atmosphere are an important factor in global climate change, which poses many threats and challenges to marine life. Many species are sensitive to changes in water temperatures and an increase of even a few degrees can trigger corals and anemones to expel their symbiotic zooxanthellae. In tropical areas, this reaction is known to cause catastrophic coral bleaching. Snakelocks anemones are an unusually northerly species to have zooxanthellae and although they are vulnerable to sudden temperature changes, they seem to show some level of adaptability to cope when the temperature change is gradual and allows them to acclimatise, which suggests they may have at least a limited ability to cope with warming seas.

The oceans play a vital role in managing atmospheric carbon dioxide levels by absorbing carbon dioxide into their surface waters. This may be good news in terms of mitigating our greenhouse gas emissions and thereby reducing the rate of temperature change, but the process also poses a severe threat to the marine ecosystem. Chemical reactions between the carbon dioxide and the seawater lower the ocean's pH, a process often referred to as ocean acidification. Corals are known to be much at risk from ocean acidification, which can reduce the rate of calcification which corals use to build their structures, and many other animals that build shells from calcium carbonate such as molluscs could be similarly affected. A change in the pH of the seawater may have some effect on the photosynthetic processes within the corals and anemones, perhaps increasing rather than decreasing them, but the exact impacts are hard to predict. A study looking at the populations of snakelocks anemones that live around underwater vents of the Vulcano volcano in Italy's Aeolian Islands has shown that their zooxanthellae algae flourish in the higher carbon dioxide concentrations, suggesting that they may be relatively resilient to changes in ocean pH, but there is much we don't yet know about how environmental changes will affect this species and the ecosystem on which it depends. However resilient one creature may be, no animal lives in isolation.

Some shallow pools are packed solid with the intertwined tentacles of many anemones, all moving and grasping for any prey that washes in. This anemone splits down the middle to reproduce, so the animals keep on dividing themselves in two and may eventually fill a pool that has sufficient nutrients. These 'urban' populations are the ones I most like to watch as they feel for prey and compete with each other for space. Any unfortunate fly that lands on the surface is instantly detected, the tentacles waving in a frenzy, firing their tiny harpoons of neurotoxin to paralyse their prey before pulling the fly under, into one of the hungry mouths beneath the surface.

The abundance of snakelocks anemones is great news for night-time rock pooling, because they have another unexpected property which make them our favourite thing to see at night. They are the main reason that Junior always packs one special piece of equipment for our expeditions: an ultraviolet torch.

Around 10 per cent of light coming from the sun is made up of ultraviolet light, a type of electromagnetic radiation with a shorter wavelength than visible light. It's called ultraviolet because it's just below violet on the spectrum. Overexposure to ultraviolet radiation can be a problem on the beach on sunny days, potentially causing sunburn and eventually skin cancer, but at night there's no risk so long as we don't shine the UV torch in each other's eyes. In the marine world there are many animals and seaweeds that fluoresce in ultraviolet light, while some others produce their own light through bioluminescence. As we move our way down the dark shore we periodically stop, turn off our head torches, and sweep the pools with the UV torch.

Often, the first thing I notice is the red seaweeds, some of which seem to glow red, purple and blue in the UV light. These seaweeds are studded with pinpricks of pink light, caused by fluorescence in the tips of the spires of grey top shells. The glow is instant, with the UV energy being absorbed by the animal or plant before being re-emitted nanoseconds later as longer-wave light. Some crabs and prawns also glow blue. Little is known about why some sea creatures fluoresce in this way, but it is generally due to the presence of certain proteins which respond in this way to ultraviolet light. Possibly this fluorescence in some

Fluorescence in a snakelocks anemone under ultraviolet light.

way protects the animal from the harmful effects of the sun's rays during daylight hours, or perhaps it sends a signal to other members of its species or other animals. There is still much we don't know about the marine world, but this doesn't bother us as we sweep the torch left and right to see what shows up.

When the beam passes over a snakelocks anemone the effect is as if an eerie green spotlight has been turned on. While the seaweed all around it remains black and invisible, or glows a deep red, the snakelocks anemone emits a green blaze of light, the sort of thing you'd expect to see in a cheap alien movie. The animal itself looks the part with its long waving tentacles too. Even from several metres away, the ultraviolet torch picks anemones out, making them far easier to find at night than by day, when they are well camouflaged among the tangle of seaweed.

There are far more snakelocks anemones than I ever realised in this sheltered gully. While the cooling sea exhales a bank of fog that consumes the shore and intensifies the silence, the ghostly lights of the fluorescing anemones guide us into the gloomy kelp

The Leach's spider crab, *Inachus phalangium*, is often found living among the tentacles of the snakelocks anemone.

beds. From the edge of a large anemone, a straw-thin spiky leg emerges, its tip scratching at the sand, followed by several more legs, glowing neon blue in the ultraviolet light. With swaying, robotic unsteadiness, the rest of the Leach's spider crab, *Inachus phalangium*, emerges, surveying the night with its stalked eyes. Its shell, covered in living sponges, appears dark in the torchlight, while the small pieces of seaweed that the crab has attached to itself as camouflage create a red glimmer around its back legs. It enjoys a commensal relationship with the anemone, which means it neither harms nor benefits the anemone in any obvious way, but the crab benefits greatly from the protection from predators that the anemone's fierce stinging tentacles offer. It also mops up any tasty scraps the anemone drops from its meals and is known to nibble on the mucus the anemone produces.

The chill of the fog and the absence of moonlight combine with the late hour to drive us homewards, retracing our sliding steps over the damp rocks. It's easy to imagine that people might become lost here at night, among this network of rocks and channels, within the confused muffling surround-sound that the descending fog creates. If we didn't know the beach so well, it would be impossible to tell whether we were moving towards or away from the sea's advancing edge. We exit through our unmarked path, and when the water rises and engulfs the anemones, we are already at home in the warm, drinking hot chocolate in our pyjamas.

CHAPTER 13

Dog Whelk

Dog whelks, despite their plain-sounding common name, are innately elegant. Their rounded shells taper into a fine spire ringed with sculpted whorls. This shape is mirrored at the base of the shell by a narrow extension, as though the dog whelk is holding its foot out *en pointe*. All of the many whelk species have this extended tear drop shape, but the dog whelk is unique in its range of bright colours and patterns, which made it a favourite in my shell-collecting days.

Rather like the flat periwinkles, dog whelks can be white, yellow, orange or brown, and sometimes sport stripes of different colours, possibly providing the population with a range of camouflage options against the rocks on which they live, which are coated in sponges and seaweeds in a variety of colours. The thickness of the shell increases with wave exposure, and while most shells are relatively smooth, with fine ridges and growth lines along their whorls, some others develop deeply grooved shells with frilly edges to their ridges, a look that's also fashionable among young dog whelks. These attractive molluscs are common around most northern European coasts, but anyone assuming that these snails led a quiet and peace-loving life akin to that of the plant-munching land snails would be much mistaken. The dog whelk is one of the deadliest predators on the shore.

The secret of the dog whelk's hunting prowess is in that elegant pointed 'foot'. For anyone new to rock pooling, the best way to identify a dog whelk is to turn it over and look at the underside of that foot. What you see is a groove, like a shallow channel, running along the protruding section of shell and open at the end. This is the animal's anterior or siphonal canal, through which it passes its feeding organ, the radula. In limpets, this toothed tongue-like organ is used to scour the rocks of tiny algae, but in the dog whelk it has been adapted to a more gruesome purpose.

Dog whelks are plentiful on our shores because their favourite prey, such as mussels, barnacles and limpets, are also numerous almost everywhere around north European coasts. They are adaptable too, and I often see them munching on top shells, periwinkles and anything else that can't move away fast enough. When the tide comes in, the dog whelks emerge from their hiding places under overhangs and in cracks in the rocks to seek out their next meal and it doesn't take them long to find it. Once positioned atop the shell of its victim, the dog whelk extends its slimy, delicate-looking proboscis containing its radula along the protective siphonal canal until it finds its target. At this point the radula emerges, covered all around in row upon row of fierce sawing teeth, and gets to work drilling into the dog whelk's prey. To make its work easier, the radula is backed up by an accessory boring organ, based in the animal's foot, which secretes chemicals onto the prey to dissolve its shell.

Unable to run away, the dog whelk's prey can often do little to stop the attack. It can probably feel the terrifying vibrations as the dog whelk's radula bores ever closer to its soft parts. The worst is yet to come.

Once the dog whelk has penetrated the animal's shell it gets to work, pumping out chemicals to drug its prey and enzymes to start the digestion process. The dog whelk's saliva glands also produce a cement-like substance that may help to hold its prey in place. The process takes a while, sometimes two or three days, during which time the dog whelk is likely to risk desiccation at low tide, but eventually the body of the unfortunate victim is reduced to a soup. The dog whelk slurps its meal up through its proboscis, before returning to its hideaway among the rocks to digest for a day or two.

On shores with the right food sources and shelter for dog whelks you can find gangs of them huddled together on the rocks, waiting for the high tide when they can carry on with their next killing spree.

Sometimes the dog whelk secures its meal by slipping its radula between the open plates of a barnacle or into a feeding clam shell, rasping the inside clean, but drilling is the main line of attack on many beaches. It's not hard to find evidence of the dog whelk's handiwork. Pick up limpet or mussel shells on almost any

Dog whelk feeding on a juvenile limpet.

beach and you will find some have a single perfectly round hole in them, just a millimetre or two across, the right size for threading with a thin needle if you were making a shell necklace.

It seems as though the dog whelk is able to terrorise the shore with impunity, but despite its stomach-churning predation skills, it is not at the top of the food chain and is readily eaten by oystercatchers and crabs, which can crush its shell, and also by eider ducks, which can swallow dog whelks whole, shell and all. However, it's not always higher predators that see off the dog whelks. The lowly mussel has developed a way to turn the tables on unwary predators.

Junior is a fan of all things gruesome, as ten-year-olds often are, so he leaps at the idea of trying to photograph a mussel attack in action. Conditions on the shore are perilous for cameras and I have written off many by dropping and scraping them against rocks, getting sand in the lens and the general corrosion that comes from working in salty water, but I have one old camera that keeps coming back to life despite my neglect. Junior likes to borrow this camera for our missions. It's a grey winter day and the tide is far from ideal. We abandon our initial plan to visit the mussel bed that encrusts Looe harbour wall because the waves are too high, forcing us to backtrack and cross the bridge to the opposite side of the river where some more sheltered rocks are just clear of the water. Some sections of rock here are black with mussels, and many more are anchored on to the rocks of the gravelly riverbed, well-positioned to catch passing food from the strong tidal inflow and outflow twice each day.

Mussels are bivalves, with shells in two halves, which means they cannot simply sucker on to rocks in the way gastropod snails do. Many species of bivalve live buried in the mud and sand to hide from predators and to stop themselves being thrown about by waves and currents, but those that live on the rocks need to find a different strategy. For oysters and some species of scallop this is solved by cementing their lower valve onto the rock, but if you touch a mussel colony, you will find that you can wiggle the shells a little. They are not cemented to the rock, but they are still firmly attached. If you move your eye in close enough, you will see that the shells are all arranged with their pointed hinge facing downwards, and that there is a tangled network of fine yellow-grey threads underneath them. Although they resemble a seaweed, these byssus threads are created by the mussels themselves, enabling them to stay on the rock and also holding them in the perfect position to open their shells up to filter feed at high tide. Search and you will find dog whelks lurking nearby. Junior finds some colourful orange and yellow dog whelks hiding in a deep crack in the rock, alongside dozens of their pink-tinged egg capsules. We're on the right track.

As the water rises, the dog whelks will emerge and set to work trying to reach or drill into the mussels' shells, but if they fail to move away fast enough it may be the last meal they ever have.

We have looked for evidence of mussels catching dog whelks on many occasions, but it can be hard to work out whether a dog whelk is truly trapped or just passing through. Junior clambers over the rocks to a half-submerged outcrop where he has spotted a thick coating of mussels and, even more promisingly, some large white dog whelks among them. Waves are pushing up the river, breaking over the rocks and washing across the mussel bed and with deep water the other side of the outcrop we have to watch our step. Balanced on the end of the outcrop, leaning over the edge, Junior points downwards. 'I think this might be one,' he calls. 'If you jump down on the ledge you can see it better.' He indicates a wave-swept step in the rock and I lower myself down until the water is surging to the top of my boots. Sadly for us, the dog whelk he's found is in perfect health and seems to

This dog whelk is ensnared by the byssus threads of the surrounding mussels.

have evaded the byssus threads to find itself a good meal. I take a photo anyway, but as I do so I notice another shell just a few centimetres away. This time there is no doubt. The dog whelk has fallen foul of the mussels.

As soon as the mussels sense a predator in their midst they start their campaign. They have no sting, no chemical weapon, no way of running away, but they do have their ability to produce byssus threads. They might not be as speedy as a spider, and they will probably never make it as a film superhero – fabulous though Mussel Woman would be – but the technique the mussels use to capture the dog whelk has much in common with the way a spider entangles its prey. By throwing out their rope-like byssus threads, the mussels aim not to move the predator on, but to trap it exactly where it is.

Held fast to the colony, trussed up in a net of byssus threads, our unfortunate dog whelk is surrounded by its food but unable to move anywhere to eat it. Slowly but surely, the dog whelk will starve to death. This one had been turned upside down by the byssus threads, exposing its body to the air, so that it looks as if it may already have been dried to death. Either way, its fate is sealed.

While dog whelks are busy sucking the life out of their fellow molluscs, their cousins the netted dog whelks, *Tritia reticulata*, are hoovering up after them. These unassuming brown snails with criss-cross patterns of ridges on their shells plough furrows through the sediment as they trawl the bottom of the pools looking for food.

Close-up, the netted dog whelk is far more remarkable than most people notice, with a huge tubular protuberance extending before it. I have always wondered if Jim Henson saw a netted dog whelk before coming up with the faces of the puppet backing singers on The Muppets' 'Manah Manah' song, because they have the same look. Grains of sand fly up as the netted dog whelk snorts and snaffles through the sand, using its long siphon to blast debris out of its way with a powerful jet of water. Receptors in its siphon taste for any food it can vacuum from the seabed as it glides back and forth, sweeping the rock pool thoroughfares clear of waste. Occasionally, a netted dog whelk will put on a turn of great speed for a snail, holding its siphon high and joining others of its kind as they all converge on a fresh piece of carrion. Any dead crab, snail or even a stranded jellyfish in its death throes will trigger a race. They pick carcasses clean, just as vultures and crows do on the land – a role that is essential to any ecosystem, however unglamorous it may seem.

These days dog whelks are not considered a commercial species, unlike their close relative, the common whelk, which lives mainly offshore and grows to a much larger size. According to an old French story, when God was in the midst of creation and had come up with good-tasting shellfish like the whelk and winkle, the devil reckoned he could do just as well and resolved to make his own version. After much effort, he created the dog whelk. He thought it was pretty good, but it couldn't rival God's great creations. The dog whelk was smaller, less impressive and didn't taste as good as God's molluscs. The story doesn't have an ending, as far as I can tell, but it does help to explain the origin of the term 'dog' whelk, or *bigorneau de chien* (dog winkle) in French, which seems to mean a lesser, or at least less edible, version of the 'original' winkle or the whelk.

While dog whelks are not about to grace any recipe books, there is significant evidence that in the past they were collected en masse. Archaeologists looking at early Christian monasteries and other sites, principally around the French and Irish coasts, have discovered large spoil heaps of dog whelk shells. These molluscs were not harvested for their taste, but probably for something else: their hypobranchial gland.

Mucus, essential to locomotion, is produced in many molluscs by the hypobranchial gland, but the gland is also responsible for producing other chemical compounds. In the dog whelk, and some other species, this includes the production of purpura, a bromine-based substance, which the snails use to sedate prey. It may also be used to protect their egg capsules from microbial attack. A clear liquid when it first emerges, this substance changes in sunlight to green, blue and finally a deep red or purple. It is known as imperial or Tyrian purple, with records of its use going back at least to Roman times, and has long been a prized dye due to the way in which its intensity increases, rather than fades, with exposure to sunlight. It is also extremely hard-wearing and difficult to wash out of clothes.

Unfortunately for the dog whelk, its hypobranchial gland can only be reached by killing the animal, ideally by breaking open the spire with a hard blow to reveal the site of the gland. The extraction process for obtaining purpura involved storing vast numbers of rotting dog whelks before boiling them in vats, occasionally skimming off the scum, and reducing the mixture in lead or tin vessels until the desired colour was obtained. In some places vats have been discovered that may have been used for this purpose, but little is known about the intricacies of how the dye was produced. It was not a process to be sniffed at – several ancient accounts of the practice refer to the horrendous stench that was emitted. As anyone who has ever picked up a dead snail will know, there are few things that smell so foul. Considerable economic gains must have motivated those who worked with the noxious fumes the dye process gave off. Dyes obtained from the dog whelk have been found in old manuscripts and textiles, and it is possible that red markings on ancient Mesolithic sites may also have come from dog whelk purpura dye. Fortunately, for the dog whelk and for human noses, the practice of extracting dye from molluscs ended in the Middle Ages.

Despite the reduction in commercial attention, in recent decades the dog whelk has faced threats from a new source. Many people will have heard of the devastating effects of the now-banned pesticide DDT on terrestrial animal and bird populations, but fewer know about the chemical tributyltin (TBT). Used extensively in anti-fouling paint on ships and marine structures up until the 1980s, TBT was highly popular and effective at preventing the growth of shipworm, barnacles and other marine creatures that would otherwise add to the weight and drag of a ship, reducing its performance. The effects of this powerful biocide were intended to be limited to the area that was painted with it, but over time the TBT leached out, percolating into the marine environment and accumulating in sediments. Studies of this chemical's effects on dog whelks helped to identify the problems it caused in the marine food chain and force a ban on its use.

Dog whelks are something of a canary in a coal mine. The dog whelk's feeding strategy may ensure that it is highly successful and well-established on most coasts, but its populations are vulnerable to changes in the environment. The key reason for this is that, unlike many other intertidal species, the dog whelk's young don't spend any time in the plankton and are therefore not widely dispersed. Each yellow and pink egg capsule, clusters of which adorn holes and cracks in the rocks, contains dozens of eggs, some of which will hatch out as baby dog whelks (the rest may well be eaten by the successful hatchlings). Neither the adults nor the babies move a long way from the laying site, so populations are very localised and cannot spread quickly. If something happens to wipe out the dog whelks on a particular beach, it may take a long time for them to re-establish.

As a predator species, the dog whelk can also be vulnerable to chemicals, like TBT, which bioaccumulate in the food chain. Such substances cannot be processed by the animal and so accumulate in their tissues, and each animal up the food chain will consume more and more of the chemicals. The further up the food chain you go, the greater the concentrations of such chemicals will be. In the same way that DDT killed birds of prey that ate smaller birds, that ate DDT-contaminated worms or insects, or DDT-covered grains, the anti-fouling paint TBT was consumed in turn by different marine animals along the food chain. It has been found in high concentrations in top predators like sea otters and dolphins, in which it is thought to affect the animal's immune system, making them more susceptible to disease.

Even though the dog whelks were lower down the food chain than marine mammals, they were observed to disappear in areas with high concentrations of ship movements and low water replacement rates, such as parts of Plymouth Sound and certain oil terminals around Orkney and Shetland. Researchers found that dog whelks were being physically altered by the ships' presence. It was discovered that TBT caused female dog whelks to grow a penis and become sterile, making reproduction impossible. The local dog whelk population was rapidly wiped out.

Initially, in the 1980s, TBT and related substances were banned only on smaller boats, but as the evidence mounted more countries imposed restrictions. It wasn't until 2008, over 20 years after the first bans, that the chemicals became subject to an international ban through the Rotterdam Convention and by the International Maritime Organization, meaning that they can only be used when sealed to prevent them from leaching into the environment. There is evidence that populations of dog whelks have recovered well, but this is just one of many salutary examples of how waste and chemicals can impact on marine species.

The idea that the oceans are vast enough to absorb anything we put into them has long been disproved and it is also self-evident that any chemical which bioaccumulates in the food chain has the potential to do the same in humans, which should be reason enough to exercise great caution. There is still much that we do not know about marine ecosystems and their sensitivities and this is even more true of the deep oceans that we are only just beginning to discover. Even a creature as common as the dog whelk can teach us a great deal.

CHAPTER 14

Goby

I'm not fond of anthropomorphising animals, but knowing that blennies look innately happy with their podgy-lipped grins while gobies always look thoroughly fed up with life, can be a great help in telling the two most common rock pool fish apart. The rock goby's huge, fleshy lips turn down at the corners and its small piggish eyes have nothing of the colour and sparkle of the shanny's. It has two separate dorsal fins, the first of which is tipped with yellow, and it is, as you might expect, the most common goby species on rocky shores. To me, the large scales on its back are instantly recognisable, giving it an almost reptilian look, and if you have the chance to look at one up-close, it also has some minute projections coming out of its nose, like tufts of nostril hair. These fish are so common on many shores that they may be taken for granted, and yet they are one of the best adapted to midshore life and tend to rule their pools.

For a true goby encounter, I don't take a net or a bucket. If I could ever remember, I'd take an extra coat to lie on, but I don't, so I make do with finding the flattest area of rock possible alongside a thigh-deep pool with some large boulders and overhangs in it. Any pool that locals call a 'swimming pool' is especially good. It's a pleasure best enjoyed alone as no group of people is capable of lying unmoving and without talking for long, and as pleasures go it's not an especially comfortable one. My top spot to search for gobies is at a south coast beach no one else seems to go to, probably because it involves scrambling down a long cliff path and there is usually a mound of rotting seaweed to wade through to access the pools, but the wild, rich shore makes it worth the effort. I prop my head on my arms, just far enough back from the water's edge to avoid being detected, and with the sun ahead of me so that my shadow isn't obvious, I settle in for the wait.

Every goby has a lair and I pass my time guessing where it might be. A small rock goby will often lurk under a slab of slate, while the larger fish go for deep overhangs and unmoveable boulders where they lie in darkness, looking out and biding their time. Deep in their hiding places, firmly attached by their specially adapted pelvic fins, which have evolved into a sucker, the goby is secure. In the intertidal world few creatures are likely to attack it, other than wading birds like herons, but when the tide comes in it can bring larger predatory fish and cormorants.

Within a few minutes of sprawling on the rocks I'm rewarded with a glimpse of a nose emerging from under a large stone. A small rock goby tests the water, then glides up, with a barely perceptible flick of its narrow tail, to rest on top of the pink encrusting seaweed that coats the boulder and bask in the sunshine.

Alongside a rock just half a metre from where I am lying, a gang of prawns has gathered around a dead shore crab. The crab looks intact and has probably only recently died. The prawns nudge each other and squabble over their pickings in their jumpy way, each intent on snatching the best morsels. One is so intent on digging out some food with its pincers that it fails to notice the other prawns scattering, and is almost crushed as the rock goby ram raids the party and grabs the crab shell, spinning with it

Matt Slater from Cornwall Wildlife Trust checking fish traps under licence.

in the style of a crocodile roll to dislodge the meat. Other gobies and blennies pile in, and by the time I leave the pool 20 minutes later there's little left of the unfortunate shore crab.

Everyone loves Cornwall Wildlife Trust's full-time marine awareness officer Matt Slater. His effervescent enthusiasm is infectious, and his knowledge of the rock pools comes not only from extensive training and experience, but from a lifelong love of the coasts he grew up on. He lives and breathes the shore, and when he's not at work he's to be found taking a spin in the waves with his surfing Labrador, Mango, or teaching children at the Holywell Bay Surf Life Saving Club. He also has a licence to trap giant gobies for conservation monitoring and his previous experience as an aquarium curator means he handles these slippery fish with far more aplomb than I could ever hope to manage. We meet to survey a beach that has the perfect habitat for giant gobies. They have never been found here before, but this is probably because no one has looked.

This is the launch day of the nascent Three Bays Wildlife Group, one of many new local marine conservation groups to spring up in recent years. It is also our first chance to survey one of the less-visited beaches in the area. Although he has seen countless thousands of shore crabs in his life, Matt talks to each child on the morning's rock pool ramble as if this were the very first and most exciting crab he's ever seen, eagerly showing them how to tell the boys from the girls and brimming with gruesome tales of the animals' lives that bring a glint to his eye. His party trick is to place a walnut between the pincers of large crabs and invite onlookers to imagine the damage the hefty claws could do to a finger. When the walnut shatters it draws horrified gasps every time.

When the public event finishes, Matt's excitement level seems to mount even further. Wasting no time, he grabs the yellow fish traps and, together with a group of local volunteers of all ages, sets off towards the clifftop path to the adjacent beach. Although the tide is already turning, we know there is still time to find a good number of species, not least of all the elusive giant goby, *Gobius cobitis*.

There are several species of goby around our coasts, many of them more sociable than the rock goby, which tends to keep away from others of its kind. The sand goby and the very similar common goby shoal around the seabed in small groups. I often see the former in the shallow pools that form on high energy sandy shores at low tide. The sea's edge is the realm of the two-spot goby, which hovers among tall strands of thong weed, often stopping just long enough to allow observers to notice its spots before zipping away. The exquisite painted goby, with its delicate spots and fine blue colouring grows to just six centimetres and is harder to see, but is worth the effort. While all of these gobies are attractive fish, I most enjoy looking for the only goby species that is larger and grumpier looking than the rock goby. At up to

27 centimetres, the giant goby is hardly a giant among fish, but is nevertheless a true Titan of the goby world. Confined, as far as we know, to the extreme south-west coasts and isles of Britain, it is also found in northern France and the Mediterranean.

This is one of the most highly protected animals in the UK, listed alongside land animals like dormice and marine animals such as dolphins, seahorses, turtles and some specialist lagoon-dwelling shrimp and snails in Schedule 5 of the Wildlife and Countryside Act 1981, which means that it is illegal to deliberately catch or trap them without a licence.

As we pass through a gate and crest the hill, an idyllic scene spreads before us. Green pastures complete with grazing sheep tumble down to a sandy bay fringed with rock pools, shielded by two headlands. A large house perches on one side, while a stream cuts through on the other. The children run ahead, down the track and the rest of us quicken our pace, hoping to explore as much as possible despite the advancing tide.

Matt wastes no time on arrival at the beach. After a quick discussion with Jeremy, a local volunteer who knows the beach well, he springs away across the rocks to set a couple of traps in the pools around the headland which look like suitable habitat, while the rest of us survey the sheltered rocks of the shore. This beach is rich in sediment and life, with plump strawberry anemones clinging to every overhang and the casts of lugworms scattered among the sand. Matt returns even more convinced that there could be giant gobies in the pools he's found. We will only be able to leave the traps down for another half hour until the tide comes in, which is not much time to catch anything, and also doesn't give us much time to find the traps again among the disorienting network of rocks and pools around the headland.

While the tide begins to swirl around our ankles, we collect some plump prawns and dig up a lugworm to show the children.

We fit in a hasty picnic, and then Matt and I grab a bucket and camera, and rush over to the rocks to check on the traps. He leaps across the top of the rocks as though there's no two-metre drop between them, while I teeter in his wake, picking less precarious routes where possible as I try to keep up. Fortunately, Matt has to stop a couple of times to get his bearings, which gives me a chance to scramble after him.

The first pool we visit is very high on the shore, without much diversity, but could just be suitable. Matt plunges an arm into the water to retrieve the baited yellow trap. He lifts it to the light and we stare through the holes, but there's nothing there, not even a shore crab. For a moment Matt just looks at the empty trap, then he scans the rocks to find the next pool. We have a couple of false starts before he recognises the rocks ahead. We know that this second fish trap might not have much in it after such a short time either, but we also know that hungry rock pool creatures are quick to snatch up any available food.

Although the trap is nestled on the bottom of a calm pool, between a large boulder and an overhang coated in pink coral weed, it is visibly moving, rolling from side to side as though it's a boat on the sea. We both draw in a sharp breath, but let it out again just as quickly as we clock the sharp leg-tips of a green shore crab poking out of the mesh. On closer inspection there are several crabs in there, fighting against the sides of the trap. Matt lifts out the trap and we gasp again. Behind the crabs and taking up most of the trap with their bulk are several gobies. All of them have the characteristic salt and pepper colouring of the giant goby. We scramble to shoo the crabs out of the trap and fill the bucket with seawater.

Once we have them in the bucket, there is no doubt that all three of these fish are giant gobies. Like the rock goby, they have pelvic fins on their underside which are adapted into a sucker to hold them fast on the rocks. The sucker fins on the fish in our

Giant goby.

bucket all sport a fleshy lobe at the front, like a small claw. This is something the rock gobies never have. The fish also lack the yellow tip to their first dorsal fin characteristic of the rock goby. The waves are starting to foam through the cracks in the rocks just beyond our pool, so we work quickly, taking photos for the species records, doing some hasty measurements and overusing the word 'awesome'.

It can take many hours of work to achieve moments like this – when we are able to record a protected species in a new location, but every time we do it builds a case for protecting that place. The giant goby is probably not a 'rare' species locally, occurring on many beaches around Cornwall alongside rock gobies, however its presence can make it harder for development or commercial activities to occur in the area, as well as making it more likely that the area could be given a special designation such as a Marine Conservation Zone.

Such protections are often weak at best, but they are what we have. To stand any chance of giving these species the protection the law is meant to afford them, we need to at least know where they live, or might be expected to live. The Cornwall Wildlife Trust's giant goby recording programme is making a massive difference to our knowledge of this one species. All around the country there are others like Matt and me, other Wildlife Trust marine teams, other marine conservation groups, research groups and tireless individuals who spend their time finding out what is there, why it's there and whether it's changing. Their voices are often drowned out by other interests, but that never stops them speaking out about what's there: what we could lose. Every discovery builds our ability to conserve the shore.

Conservation value aside, it is an incredible thing to meet a goby of this size, to look into the deep-set eyes and downturned mouth of the undisputed ruler of the midshore Cornish pools. Given the restrictions on disturbing this species, coming this close to one is a rare moment. It's impressive for us to see them, but our three giant gobies are unimpressed by being taken from the cage, where they were happily feasting on the bait before winding up in our bucket. We waste no time in returning them to the safety of their domain, where they disappear in a flash.

As we clamber away from the pool, I look back and see a giant goby's head lurking in the shadow of a boulder on the floor of the pool, no doubt making sure we have left. Meanwhile the waves over-top the rocks and bubble into the pool, covering up the shore's secrets once more.

CHAPTER 15

Lugworm

A distant figure moves ponderously across the exposed muddy sand, steps weighed down by outsized boots, loose overalls and the weight of the tall metal fork. Lazy wingbeats carry wading birds on their oblique flight across the shore, away from the human, who sets a bucket down on the sediment. Shrill fluting cries rise and fall.

Reading the mud in the same way as the birds, the digger picks a spot, plunges the fork in and draws up the sulphurous ooze beneath. A fat lugworm is tossed into the bucket and the solitary figure scans the ground for the next target.

It is a sight almost as old as time, and one that plays out on sediment shores every day across the country and beyond. Small scale harvesting of lugworms for use as fishing bait has been taking place for many centuries. The reason anglers target lugworms is that they are numerous, easy to find and they are meaty enough to attract large fish like flatfish.

As they spend most of their lives completely hidden in their horseshoe-shaped burrow beneath the surface, the only evidence most people ever see of the lugworm's existence is an inelegant heap of dark but inoffensive faecal matter deposited on the sand:

a worm cast. If you dig up a lugworm's burrow, you will find that it is lined in paler sediment than the surrounding anoxic muddy sand. The dense, dark mud is full of organic material, but lacks the flow of air and water that provide the oxygen required by most lifeforms to survive. Instead, bacteria that breathe sulfates go to work decomposing the organic matter, releasing hydrogen sulfide in the process, which gives the sediment a distinctive smell of rotten eggs. The lugworms alter that environment by oxygenating their burrows.

On suitable beaches the entire surface of the mid and lower shore can be strewn with these muddy piles. Next to each heap a round depression in the sand is often visible, as though a minute sinkhole has opened up. This is the worm's feeding funnel. The animal's head is positioned well beneath the surface, drawing in sediment containing the detritus on which it feeds, causing the sediment above to collapse inwards a little. Simultaneously it pumps water from tail to head, irrigating its burrow and drawing in oxygen-rich sediment from near the surface. Every time the

The depression and waste pile mark the two ends of a lugworm's burrow.

worm pokes its tail out of the other end of its burrow to defecate, it takes a risk. With no eyes in that end of its body, it has no idea what might be about. Lugworm tails are a favourite snack of inshore flatfish like the flounder.

On a calm day with an outgoing tide, I often watch lugworm burrows to see the glugging movement of the head drawing matter into the sand burrow, or the casts forming on the surface. Unglamorous as they seem, lugworms are a vital food source for curlews, oystercatchers and bar-tailed godwit at low tide, and for all sorts of fish at high tide. Their burrows also increase the rate of decomposition in the substrate due to their higher oxygen content compared to the surrounding sediment, a process called bioturbation. They provide a habitat for some small invertebrates including several species of flatworm, which would not otherwise be able to survive here.

It can be challenging to convince people that worms are worth a second look, especially ones with no exciting-looking features like the humble lugworm. A 20-centimetre, fat, pink worm with clumps of bristly looking gills down its muddy sides that can shoot out a proboscis in the shape of a balloon neck, is not the obvious place to start.

Undeterred, the Capturing Our Coast partnership of marine conservation experts and research organisations launched the unforgettably named Spermwatch project in 2016. As community engagement projects go, it was starting from a challenging place, but the great British public is a surprising thing. Over two years, hundreds of surveys were completed by individuals and groups who walked the beaches in search of sperm puddles.

Sperm puddles are exactly what they sound like: milky-white splashes of lugworm sperm in midshore sand next to lugworm casts. The lugworm's reproduction method is imprecise but effective. The male worms squirt sperm out onto the sand and let it wash with the tide into the burrows of female lugworms.

Although it is known that lugworms broadcast their sperm en masse, soaking the beaches in the stuff, no one has been sure what triggers such events. In some areas it happens twice a year, with different parts of the local population spawning at different times, and in most places it happens only once a year. It may be brought on by the joys of spring in some areas, taking place as late as April, but spawning usually takes place during the autumn.

By mapping where and when the lugworms eject their sperm, Spermwatch is building a more accurate picture of regional variations. It is far from easy to capture evidence of spawning because it happens so infrequently and tides and weather conditions can make access difficult or wash away the evidence, yet the project was successful in gathering some useful records. In 2017, spawning was seen by volunteers at nine locations, with southern sites showing a tendency to commence spawning at higher sea temperatures than northern ones. This research matters because lugworms are a crucial part of the ecosystem and are especially important as a food source for wading birds and for flatfish, therefore their numbers can affect fish stocks. The sensitivity of the spawning event to temperature may mean that changes in sea temperature and timing of the seasons could affect the lugworm's spawning patterns.

Spermwatch is not the only scientific project with an interest in lugworms. This worm's ability to spend many hours at a time out of water in the anoxic environment of the muddy sediment is down to a very special adaptation. The worm's haemoglobin, the substance responsible for transporting oxygen around the body, is able to carry around 40 times more oxygen than a human's. In this way, the worm tops up on oxygen when there is water available in its burrow and uses it up gradually in times of shortage. Medical researchers in France are hoping that this special property could be transferred into human blood, acting as a replacement for a patient's own haemoglobin, to help people with heart disease who suffer from low oxygen levels in the blood and those recovering from transplant operations in whom increased oxygen levels improve recovery rates. It may also be a way of prolonging the life of human organs destined for transplant. Lugworm haemoglobin is compatible with all human blood types, a quality that makes it particularly interesting to researchers, but its properties would presumably need to be copied synthetically. It would take a lot of lugworms to produce a pint of blood and they would be unlikely to be given a cup of sweet tea and a Club biscuit for their time. The concept of harnessing their powers is, however, a potentially brilliant one.

Worms are clearly complex and surprising animals, so to look at them only in terms of their utility to humans is to miss the point. These incredible properties and abilities have evolved to enable these worms to survive in the most extreme circumstances possible.

If lugworms aren't your thing, there is still every chance you will find a marine worm that grabs your attention. Flatworms, ribbon worms and 'true' annelid worms abound in such an amazing variety of shapes, colours and lifestyles that it is impossible not to be intrigued by them. Many marine annelid worms are polychaetes (bristle worms) that have leg-like parapodia covered in bristles, which they use to swim or walk around the sea floor.

You could do worse than to start with the king ragworm, *Alitta virens,* another worm that is often used by anglers as bait, and which is therefore rarely appreciated for the incredible animal it is.

My first encounter with one of these beasts was on the Gann Estuary in Wales during a week-long Field Studies Council event dedicated entirely to worms in the early 2000s. It wasn't a group of animals I had paid much attention to previously, largely because the sheer number of species made trying to identify them a daunting task, but there was something fascinating about the diversity of shapes and colours and habitats that drew me to them. I had been working in cities for several years by that point, flitting between London and Manchester as different opportunities arose. Although I had learned many things about writing briefing papers, surviving long meetings and making sense of Microsoft Project software, I had a constant nagging feeling that none of it mattered, or at least not to me.

Incredibly, I was not alone in wanting to spend my time looking at worms and the other people on my course were all young and keen. They were involved in marine recording either through their work or by volunteering with organisations such as the National Trust, which manages more than 775 miles of the UK's coastline. Although we associate estuaries with mud, the Gann also has a variety of other habitats including a rocky reef, making it perfect for finding a whole gamut of marine worms in a short time. It helped that our tutor, Phil, was so knowledgeable and passionate about his subject. Everyone he worked with seemed to know him as 'the worm man'.

We piled out of the minibus, hauling buckets, sieves and forks with us, exploring the firm muddy sediment towards the edges of the channel, working our way out with the falling tide. On the midshore mud we searched for the telltale hole marking the burrow of a ragworm. Ragworm is a loose term, covering a range of species belonging to various families, but all have a long, flattened body, fringed with many bristly parapodia down the length of their body, making them appear more like a millipede than an earthworm. The hole itself was not easy to see and there was no cast next to it pointing the way, but as we approached, a small jet of water shot up drawing our attention to the burrow, suggesting that it belonged to a considerable-sized occupant. Phil grabbed a fork.

The heap of mud that he swiftly dug out and dumped at his feet was putrid, dark and had a smell somewhere between well-rotted seaweed and a volcanic vent, but a paler line cut through it: the worm's burrow. Writhing in the middle of it, and starting to make off at remarkable speed, was the largest worm I'd ever seen, almost as long as a school ruler and as robust-looking. I hesitated to pick it up, but Phil thrust his hand straight into the mud, gripped it behind its head like a snake and dropped it in a bucket of water.

The metallic sheen I glimpsed among the mud was unveiled in its full glory as the water swept the mud off the worm's back. It swam through the water in a shivering wave of movement, giving off iridescent flashes of mesmerising oily green, alternating with dark ocean-blue. Out of the light it was almost black.

'Take a look at this,' Phil said, beckoning us to come in close. Producing something stick-like from his pocket, possibly a pencil, he proceeded to place the tip of it in front of the worm's head.

King ragworm. *APHOTOMARINE*

What happened next was shocking enough, but became all the more so when viewed down a microscope back at the laboratory afterwards.

As we watched, the worm's head opened up like a widening camera shutter, and the centre of it expanded in front of our eyes, before closing on the pencil. Clearly this huge proboscis that had just catapulted itself out of the creature's head bore its jaws. This made me even less likely to try to pluck one out of the mud, especially given the worm's ability to bend in an infinite number of ways and directions to line up with a nearby finger.

Like all creatures on the shore, though, the ragworm had little interest in scaring me. Its pincer jaws, set at the tip of the proboscis, are the perfect design for its feeding technique. These large worms need to put away substantial amounts of food, including detritus and small animals, but they prefer not to leave the safety of their burrows unless food is in short supply. Instead, they stick their heads out to forage, telescoping out their jaws to their full extent and sweeping about to catch their targets and drag food down into their lairs.

Occasionally, king ragworms emerge from their burrows to swim across the sediment in search of detritus to eat or perhaps to broadcast their sperm, and this is when I occasionally see one. Their undulating swimming pattern and colours deeper and brighter than the ocean itself are a captivating sight. For a worm that spends almost its entire life hidden from view, it is amazingly beautiful; something I contemplate every time I witness it. King ragworms never abandon their burrows for long, returning swiftly at the slightest sign of danger. In tests they have been shown to respond to chemical signals of flatfish in the area, smelling out the predators and withdrawing. If they smell a dead ragworm in the vicinity, the effect is even more rapid as they turn on their tail and snake straight back to their holes.

Worldwide, ragworms for bait are a multibillion-pound industry, and while many are still dug using traditional methods, commercial ragworm farming has become a serious business in some countries. One ragworm farm in Holland produces over 100 tonnes of worms per year, which are distributed worldwide to anglers and to shrimp farms where they are used as feed. This sort of production hasn't yet taken off in the UK, but commercial and amateur bait digging have grown. Although bait digging can increase the density of worms in an area, perhaps by removing the larger worms and reducing competition for food and space, it is not all good news. Uncontrolled bait digging can have a detrimental impact on the whole ecosystem by disturbing the oxygenated ragworm burrows that provide a habitat for a variety of life. Digging may also disturb wading birds that feed in these areas and reduce their food supply. If bait diggers back-fill their holes, the worms themselves are likely to recover well, but some species, such as certain urchins and bivalves like cockles and mussels, are less able to re-establish. It is in anglers' as well as conservationists' interests to take high levels of bait digging in sensitive areas seriously, because changes in the ecosystem may result in fewer fish.

By the end of my week-long worm workshop, my view of these mysterious animals was transformed. Everywhere on the shore and everywhere in the ocean there are worms. Bright-green paddleworms, so long that they loop themselves around mussels as they travel across the rocks, are everywhere on the midshore. Brilliant black and white candy-striped flatworms twist and twirl their way through the water. Some worms swim as actively as fish, others sense the world through huge clusters of dark eyespots, while others give you a surprising nip when you inadvertently lean against the openings to the tubes they have built to hide in among the rocks. The furry-looking sea mouse, a worm made of flat scales but so thickly fringed in long hairs that there is nothing about it that makes you think of a worm, is perhaps the most surprising of all. It takes its scientific name, *Aphrodita aculeata*, from the Greek goddess of love, Aphrodite. Every hair on this little love-mouse's ten-centimetre body catches the light and glows red, blue and green, shining out of the sand as it snuffles its way along. Like the ragworm, it spends most of its time buried completely or partly in the sand and its colours are a mystery, simply a consequence of the structure of the hairs and serving no known purpose.

Whether you are on a sandy, muddy or rocky shore, and whether the conditions are sheltered or exposed, worms of some sort will be close at hand. On some exposed southern coasts, the bulging colonies of sand-built tubes of the honeycomb worm cover the rocks, as if they have been invaded by nesting bees. Under loose stones at low tide, bootlace worms can be found as knotted black bundles, their bodies so long they become a tangle, and when fully extended can be many metres long – holding the Guinness World Record for the Longest Animal. One specimen found in St Andrews in 1864 was purported to measure over 55 metres, making it far longer than the blue whale. I've never seen one anything like that length though and most are probably around 5 to 15 metres long.

The strange and varied worms of the shore couldn't be further from the familiar earthworm in their appearances and lifestyles. Although they are not as popular with rock poolers as crabs, fish and starfish, they are more than worthy of our attention.

CHAPTER 16
Clingfish

It's not unusual for marine biologists to pair up for life, like albatrosses or seahorses. It's a sensible way of to finding someone who might be willing to put up with spending hundreds of hours on windswept beaches, or days and weeks travelling on diving boats. I have always assumed that this practical approach to choosing a mate is responsible for enabling the creation of the useful introductory tome, *A Student's Guide to the Seashore*, whose authors are both named Fish.

Not having studied marine biology at university myself, I seem to have missed the boat for selecting a partner by picking from my cohort, which is probably for the best in all sorts of ways.

My family today is full of obsessives, so rock pooling has to compete with Junior's fixation with volcanoes and brass band music, Ed's interest in all things aerospace and a host of other commitments in the diary. Our interests mostly balance each other out but Junior, who loves the beach, does sometimes remind me that you can have too much of a good thing, especially towards the end of a week-long survey in freezing water searching for just one species. There are benefits to learning about each other's worlds though: I have explored a full-scale model of the

International Space Station, climbed an erupting volcano and am learning to play the cornet with our local brass band. Some of these experiences have been more comfortable than others, but they have all broadened my world and I have repaid my family by enabling them to come face to face with sharks and jellyfish, whether they like it or not.

There are days when even I feel reluctant to spend time on an exposed beach, especially in high winds and the sort of Cornish mizzle that doesn't look like rain but soaks you in minutes and seeps in at every seam. On most other days, however, the beach is as good a place as any for a family expedition into the unknown. My other half and son may not be as entranced as I am by minuscule sea spiders and hydroids, but they love nothing better than a good fish hunt, and they have a far higher success rate than I ever will.

To me, fish are often the things that zoom away while I'm trying to take a sharp photo of a worm, or that slap water into my face with their tails while I'm lifting seaweed to search for molluscs. I love to watch fish and to see them up close, but I'm quick to accept defeat when they're in a large pool with plenty of hiding spots. The rest of the family, on the other hand, shout 'Death or glory!' and fling themselves into pursuit of any fish that crosses their path. So it is that, on our days out together, I am frequently summoned to look at whatever fish they have managed to corner or scoop into a bucket: slippery rocklings with barbels sprouting from their chins, colourful wrasse, silver sand eels, grinning blennies and, their favourite, the shore (or Cornish) clingfish, *Lepadogaster purpurea*.

The sucker fin of the giant goby may look impressive, but it cannot begin to compete with the strength of the clingfish's suction cup. By fusing together its pelvic fins to make a rounded sucker under the front half of its belly, these fish can weld

Cornish clingfish.

themselves onto a rock with a force that comes close to rivalling the limpet. The secret is in the ring of barely visible hexagonal shapes that fringe the sucker, each of which is made of many tiny hair-like structures. These 'hairs' create friction that makes the fish's grip almost impossible to dislodge – a technique very similar to that used in the feet of geckos to enable them to climb vertical surfaces. Some clingfish can support up to 300 times their own weight, making them ideally adapted to surviving strong currents, winter storms and attempts by predators to dislodge them from their rocky homes. When they choose to clamp down, there is no point trying to coax them into a bucket. They invariably stay put in the knowledge that they are safe where they are.

Many fish of the shore are decked out in plain, mottled brown colours, and those that often swim out at sea are more likely to have shiny or dark colours above and white underneath, to minimise their chances of being seen by birds from the air or larger fish from below. The clingfish never received that memo. It has found its own uniquely stylish ways to be camouflaged in its environment. For a start, it refuses to follow the mottling trend and has opted for a bold leopard-print pattern of brown spots all over its back and right down to the tail section of its body, colours which contrast with the bright red dorsal fin that runs down the lower half of its narrow back almost to the tip of its neat, square tail. All of this, however, is just a kind of display cushion for the fish's most arresting feature. Its feline spots widen into dark rings at the back of its wide head, to frame its jewels: two shining circles of glittering turquoise.

The fish's prow tapers into a flat rounded platform like a duck's bill, which is often a deep red colour to match its dorsal fin. The clingfish watches all movement attentively through its bulbous orange eyes, fringed each side of its nose with a feathery tentacle, positioned like windscreen wipers.

There are many bold and unexpected colours on the shore, but the clingfish is supremely striking. When fully grown and sitting serenely on a rock, it is one of the most ideal photographic models you will find in the marine world.

Like the other fish of this zone, the clingfish is well able to survive changing oxygen levels and to cope with being out of the water for a while. Gripping on to the damp substrate is also a useful strategy to avoid drying out. Clingfish may lie so unmoving that they seem part of the rock, but in a blink they thrash their tails and dart away, flitting between rocks in the style of a quantum leap, seeming to appear in a new position without moving from the first.

The other, smaller species of clingfish found in the intertidal zone may not be able to rival the azure crown of the Cornish clingfish, but they have their own styles, adorned in red, or turquoise spots, or sporty white headbands. The most mesmerising of all is the Connemara clingfish, with its cartwheel-striped eyes and matching stripy lips; it is an elusive fish which is worth waiting for.

The problem for any rock pooler who catches a clingfish in a small tub or, worst of all, a large bucket, is that the fish's natural instinct is to swim to the bottom and sucker on for dear life.

For all their prowess in catching fish, my family seems to lose interest when it comes to releasing clingfish. They're happy to hold a bucket in a pool to let an eel or goby swim free, but if they catch a clingfish, I am normally handed the bucket while they skip off to unwrap the picnic. With luck, if the tub is held in the water close to some rocks, the clingfish will make a sudden dash for safety, but more often it retains its grip even as the tide wells up around the top of my wellies. The fish would contentedly stay in that position for hours without some persuasion. The technique I use is rather like sheep herding with my hands as the sheepdogs. I block any retrogressive moves towards the bottom of the bucket, while applying just enough pressure to the fish's side, or under its sucker to convince it to edge forwards. It can be a slow job and often goes wrong at the end, when the fish darts back to its original position, or takes up residence on the outside of the bucket instead. It's a situation best avoided, but it does create a healthy respect for the fish's abilities.

Clingfish may be present on the shore all year, but it is between the late spring and early summer that I become gripped by the need to seek them out. Like other fish which lay their eggs on a solid surface rather than broadcasting them into the plankton, clingfish tend to stay close to their eggs. They are more egalitarian than other species, in that either the male or the female can take on guard duties. Like the parents, the eggs are well turned out, laid neatly in a perfectly tessellated pattern of overlapping spheroids. When freshly laid under a stone, they are a bright, golden yellow and glow like fairy lights if they catch the sun. Once I find a clutch of egg treasure like this, I return regularly, knowing that they will undergo a transformation of inverted alchemy from gold to silver as the weeks progress. The colour change is obvious to the naked eye, but it is the magic happening inside the egg that stops my heart every time I see it through a hand lens or through my camera's macro.

A remote cove around a two-mile walk from my home is my usual destination for observing clingfish eggs, but there are many more clingfish-spotting shores all around south-west England, Wales, Ireland and south-west Scotland. On the muddy footpath across the cliffs I am alone, even though the town is barely 500 metres behind me. Over distant fields, the first skylarks of the season sing through the clear air while, closer at hand, a raven weaves its messy flight path over the bay, its gruff calls echoing off the lonely cliffs. I scramble down the slippery slope, descend the steps to the bay and slide over the exposed rocks to an inlet that is home to dozens of Cornish clingfish.

However hard I try to memorise the location of clutches of eggs, however much I look at the shape of the rocks or the pattern of pools around me, and no matter how carefully I triangulate by lining up a rock that looks like a dragon's nose with the fence post nearest the cliff or whatever other landmarks are available, I always find myself lost and unsure. There's no one else to ask. The beach is almost deserted – there's just the usual band of oystercatchers on the rocks near the point and a lone cormorant that keeps slipping below the waves, led towards unseen fish by its long neck.

In the knowledge that there are precious eggs under the rocks, I am even more attentive than usual to moving the rocks slowly, making sure I have a firm enough grip not to drop them. I find several clingfish sheltering in the seaweed before I locate the first eggs. This clutch seems to be maturing well as the eggs are lighter in colour than before. I work fast. Even when the rock is angled away from the sun and wind, time is of the essence if I want to take photos without any risk of them drying out. Life is tough enough on the shore without a blundering rock pooler making things any worse.

I crouch on the damp seaweed, ignoring my cold knees, adjust my camera until the magnification is enough to see each individual egg, and tune the focus. The screen transforms in an instant from blurry circles to something arresting. Wide eyes rimmed in metallic green stare out from each egg. These baby fish are close to hatching and some are wriggling inside their eggs, preparing to unwrap their spotted tails that encircle them like winter scarves and swim free. To find the eggs is itself exciting, but to see these new lives developing in all their incredible colours is breath-taking. I am about to return the rock to its resting place, knowing that next time I return there will be only empty eggs, when I notice something else in the viewfinder. Nestled among its siblings is a hatchling that has left its egg but not yet deserted the safety of its peers. Without the covering sheen of the egg, its colours look different. The whole body is spotted from head to tail and its eyes are a hazy sky blue, rimmed not with green, but with pure gold.

When these babies swim away from the nest and from their parents' protection they will face many dangers. I most likely won't see them again until they are young adults, back on this shore, and only a few of them will make it that far.

The fate of the next brood I visit has already been sealed. All but half a dozen eggs have been cracked open and on one side of the clutch only a pattern of yellow circular stains marks the spot where the eggs once were. For a moment I hope that the baby clingfish, whose development I've been following since before their bodies took shape, must have emerged earlier than I expected. Then I see the meandering stream of white that runs

Clingfish eggs with a recently hatched baby fish in the centre.

through the ruins of the laying site. My eyes roam left and right and what I see confirms what I already know: the white strands are the spawn of *Calma glaucoides*, a sea slug. The slug has feasted on the fish eggs before replacing them with its own eggs.

That even the golden-eyed baby clingfish, still in their eggs, are part of the food chain is difficult to stomach, but such are the realities of the natural world, and despite its unpleasant eating habits this slug is impressive in its own right. The sides of its body are fringed in long steely-blue strands tipped with yellow, like a long shag-pile rug. These cerata are where digestion takes place and also act as the slug's gills. Little is known about the life cycle of the *Calma* slugs. Fish eggs are available for only a short period of the year, so the slugs must survive somewhere between times, whether in the plankton or on some other food source, but there have been few sightings of them anywhere but on fish eggs.

I place the rock in the water to watch the sea slug glide across the fragmented remains of the clingfish's eggs. Somehow it has managed to slip through the clingfish's defences and wreak this destruction without being detected. It is a beautiful beast, with its long fringe swaying in the current, but the golden tips of the cerata always remind me of clingfish eyes. I reflect, with horror, that many slugs are able to store colours from their prey in their bodies. The golden yellow in the slug unsettles me, as though the fish eyes might still be looking out: lonely beaches can play tricks on the mind. I decide to replace the stone.

Records of *Calma glaucoides* around our shores are few and sparse, and records of its relative that feeds on the eggs of gobies are even scarcer, but this may simply be because few people are looking for them. There is much we don't know about even these animals of the midshore, which are relatively accessible and easy to observe, and as we move towards the lower shore even greater mysteries beckon.

With so much to find out about our shores, who knows what remains to be discovered about the deeper oceans?

PART THREE

GATEWAY TO THE DEEP

The Lower Intertidal Zone

We are reaching the limits of our journey. The ever-shifting seas will soon block our path, but during the lowest tides we can explore parts of the seabed that are underwater for almost every hour of every day of the year. Gone are the challenges of the upper and midshore: the lower shore is only rarely exposed to the drying forces of the sun and wind and the animals that live here are not faced with such changeable temperatures, variable salinity or plummeting oxygen levels. However, the stakes remain at least as high here at the edge of the vast marine world. An incredible diversity of life has evolved in our shallow seas, creating a finely tuned ecosystem where every species must contend with competition, predators or parasites in its fight to survive.

The battles, triumphs and explosions of colour and speed in this rarely seen world rival the greatest of terrestrial wilderness scenes. Armies of huge, well-armoured spider crabs come and go, grazing herds of sea hares and snails surge through the great forests of multicoloured seaweeds that rise every summer and die back each winter. Balling shoals of young pilchards and herring are chased to the water's edge by hungry mackerel, making the sea boil and tremble. Catsharks lay their eggs here, 15-spined sticklebacks build their nests and lobsters, cuttlefish and curled octopus hunt. The brightest corals hide in the booming caves of wild beaches, perfectly camouflaged weever fish and flatfish lurk among the sands, urchins and sea cucumbers scour the rocky reefs and forms of life that most people never meet – hydroids, sea squirts, sponges, sea mats and more – coat every available surface. Jellyfish, hydroid medusae, Portuguese man o'war and delicate violet bubble snails sweep through the waters, at the mercy of the winds and currents that carry them towards the shore.

There are weapons and defences everywhere. Stings, teeth, acids, spines, pincers, smoke screens and sticky threads abound. Animals are encrusted in yet more living things, predators hide in plain sight, parasites replace the tongues of living fish and nothing is safe. The fight for life is cruel and vibrant.

Our northern European waters are far from the dingy soup that some might imagine. Apart from the myriad of colours in the seaweeds, there are pink and yellow sponges; scarlet and gold cup corals; emerald green chameleon prawns; midnight-blue lobsters; iridescent worms; red-striped brittle stars; anemones of the brightest turquoise, white, red and pink; sheets of blue and yellow sea squirts; and floating by come the coloured fairy lights of the comb jellies and the silver darts of sand eels, which hop and scoot along the water's surface like shooting stars.

What we cannot see is just as incredible as what we can see. Sometimes the water is so thick with microscopic plankton that it becomes visibly cloudy. In this churning broth of life there are minute seaweeds and animals, some of which will settle to become the crabs, prawns, barnacles and snails of tomorrow's shores, while others spend their whole lives drifting in this way. In summer the shores can light up with the blue glow of the bioluminescent plankton known as sea sparkle, while the warm water can also cause a devastating red tide of dinoflagellates, a type of microscopic algae which can release toxins that are deadly to other marine life.

This vicious, colourful, precarious sub-tidal world does not give up its mysteries easily. Usually only divers can visit, and even they are limited by the amount of air in their tanks. Rock poolers on foot, however, can visit the lower shore provided we are mindful of the tides, aware of conditions, vigilant of the swell and prepared for every weapon that the weather can throw at us. We must also be careful not to damage the delicate animals that are easily trampled underfoot or to be stung or bitten. On a hot summer's day, when I can slip on my beach shoes and shorts to wade among the fish, there is nothing more uplifting than standing in this haven of colour and diversity, never knowing what I might see next. In the winter, the pools themselves are just as intoxicating, even if my progress is encumbered by the number of layers I have to squeeze under my roomy waders.

Despite the challenges of accessing the lowest reaches of the shore, I am not alone in believing that the pain is worth it. Rock pooling on the lower shore may not be glamorous, but it is exciting.

CHAPTER 17

Sea Squirt

You know that you are encroaching on the underwater world
when you meet animals that seem to have nothing in common
with any land animal. It is hard enough to comprehend a sea
anemone as an animal when you first encounter a blob of jelly on
the rock, but when you watch it moving its tentacles to ensnare
prey, it becomes clear that for all its weirdness there is something
recognisably animalian about it. Understanding a sea squirt as
an animal is far more challenging. It stretches the imagination
beyond its twanging point.

Like anemones, sea squirts are essentially blobs to our eyes.
They come in different sizes and different colours; some are
rounded, others are flat sheets of jelly, some are transparent,
some are thick-skinned and gnarled, but they are all essentially
blobs. Unlike anemones, no matter how long you watch our
intertidal sea squirts, whether in or out of the water, they are
unlikely to visibly do very much.

Sea squirts are named after their squirting reflex. Despite
their sessile nature, if you lean in too close to look at one, you
may feel the full power of that water-squirting mechanism
straight in the eye. In fact it is tempting to prod these animals to

make them squirt, but sea squirts are easily damaged and are best left alone.

The secret to the sea squirt's ability to unleash a jet of water is in its light and pressure-sensitive organs. These often appear as red pinprick spots around the two round openings of the animal's siphons. Most of the time, one of the siphons draws water into the body, passing it through a sticky mucus on the animal's digestive organs to separate out the minute phytoplankton, bacteria and other organic debris on which it feeds, before expelling the water through the other siphon. The system works efficiently, but the gaping holes in the siphon which allow food in can also provide predators with direct access to the animal's innards and, unlike most animals on the shore, the sea squirts have no claws, teeth, armour nor stinging tentacles. Their main line of defence is to notice the approach of a predator and close up shop, presenting only their unappetising exterior to any passing carnivore. Any rapid movement or suspicious change in light near their siphon will cause the squirt to contract its body, narrow its siphon and force out a jet of high-pressure water longer than the animal itself. These tiny fountains occasionally take me by surprise and would probably make any predator start as well. Any animal too big to digest that falls into a squirt's siphon, will find itself forcefully ejected by this method too.

Not all sea squirts are obvious squirty blobs; there are others that form thin sheets of joined animals that work together as a colony. I can happily spend an hour collecting photos of sea squirt colonies on stony beaches where the clear water ensures a perfect view and the rocks are free of sediment.

Even in its most common colour form, there are few things more photogenic than the star ascidian, *Botryllus schlosseri*. It isn't difficult to find. A short perusal of the lower shore rocks, overhangs and seaweeds usually turns up a colony within minutes

An especially starry-looking star ascidian sea squirt colony.

and, if I'm lucky, I haul over a boulder to find that almost the entire underside is covered with a deep violet, the colour of a summer night sky, studded with white stars. Whole rocks can be carpeted in heavenly constellations. I walk among the stars and take photos, while fish flit past my feet and waves exhaust themselves on the rocks around me. Sometimes the background colour is a vivid blue, as though dawn is breaking behind the stars.

As I explore the pools, I find a frond of kelp with a circle of saffron yellow star ascidian on it, the stars appearing more like pale flowers in a summer meadow. Another is the crimson of a sprouting desert after the rain, with yellow petals scattered across it, while another still is a snow field of white and grey.

These minute pale 'petals', usually arranged into groups of five in flowering circles, are individual animals. It is impossible to see into their opaque bodies, but each arm of each 'star' in the star ascidian has its own heart, digestive system and reproductive organs, with a siphon hole at the end of the animal's body to draw in water containing food. At the centre of every star is a rounded hole, a shared siphon, through which all the colony's waste is expelled. These minute organisms pool their resources and energy and the flowers can also bud new petals asexually to expand the colony.

On a larger patch I notice movement. It seems that the squirt colony is flowing, edging inwards on itself. The star ascidian itself is anchored to the rock and can go nowhere and yet I can see a creeping movement. The same thing is happening on the opposite side of the colony. Only under the camera's macro setting can I see that these are flatworms, even thinner than the layer of star ascidian, perfectly camouflaged with sparkling, speckled edges, closely resembling the edges of the sea squirt colony. The flatworms' bodies seem transparent. It is impossible to see where the worm ends and its prey begins. As the worms glide across the smooth surface of the squirt their outlines come and go. These *Cycloporus papillosus* worms specialise in eating sea squirts from the *Botrylloides* genus but, for obvious reasons, not many people see them.

By the end of an hour, I have found four different colour combinations of star ascidian living on every type of surface. They even make their home on the egg cases of catsharks. Sometimes, I'm lucky enough to see the central siphon of a colonial group opening and closing, puffing out unwanted material, but mostly they do nothing that we can perceive, except decorate the rocks with their striking geometric designs.

Nestled under the surface of a shady pool, beneath a shelving overhang of slate so thickly encrusted with life that only a few recent limpet scars expose the bare blue rock, I half-notice a group of squirts. Although my eye settles on them, I must move my head back and forth like a curious owl to be able to focus on these transparent animals clustered so close together that I cannot see a space between them. A straight yellow line runs up either side of each individual like narrow cables, meeting at the top in pale circular patterns. The yellow strands beneath the glassy transparent outer body are strikingly like the glowing filaments of an old-fashioned light bulb. *Clavelina lepadiformis* is unsurprisingly known as the light-bulb sea squirt and it is often found in groups like this. I separate the individuals in this cluster and across the rock beneath them is a network of thin white stolons that root the colony in place and from which new members sprout.

Unlike the star ascidian, every animal in this light bulb sea squirt colony has siphons of its own. I can see the animal's organs through its transparent body, including the branchial sac – the organ which beats tiny hairs called cilia to force the water to flow through the squirt's body. Inside those siphons, the squirt makes sticky mucus in a never-ending production line to ensure it is able to trap food. Deep inside the sea squirt, near its base, is a bright yellow stain, too small to see in detail, which is the squirt's brood chamber and a dark line is the animal's gut.

Light-bulb sea squirts.

While, like the star ascidian, these sea squirts can reproduce by budding, they still need to reproduce sexually to ensure the settlement of new colonies, so they keep their eggs safely inside them until they are ready to hatch and join the plankton. Like many other marine creatures, the sea squirts hedge their bets and have both male and female organs.

As I touch the sea squirts to examine them, a predator, a large candy-striped flatworm, unfurls and unhurriedly undulates through the water, flashing its wide white underbelly. The seven dark stripes stretching from the back of its head to its tail twist and stretch as it glides and flaps past.

Sea squirts provide rich pickings for all sorts of worms, molluscs and sea slugs, despite their tough external skin-like structure known as a tunic or test. These predators are specially adapted to find a way through the squirts' limited defences. Some solitary sea squirts are known to produce acids to provide them with a further line of defence, but those on the shore generally rely on their unappetising casings and their squirt mechanism.

The simplicity of the sea squirt and its ability to spread through the plankton have made it a successful coloniser of new substrates. Some species have appeared with remarkable rapidity in new locations and can quickly take over if left unchecked. I now frequently see the orange-tipped sea squirt, *Corella eumyota*, which only arrived in the UK in 2004. A native of Australia, New Zealand and other coasts close to the Antarctic, this species is best recognised by the horseshoe of faecal matter visible in its twisted gut through the animal's transparent test. It probably arrived with imported shellfish or on the hulls of ships, but is now a regular occurrence in northern Spain, France and southern Britain, and as far north as Rathlin Island in Northern Ireland and Northumberland in England.

Visit almost any busy working harbour or marina and the situation can be dire, with large numbers of *Corella eumyota* and other invasive sea squirts building up under pontoons, on rocks and even on the hulls of boats. The carpet sea squirt, *Didemnum vexillum*, arrived in 2008 from the north-west Pacific and is causing concern. As the name suggests, it grows in a thick, smothering sheet, and is capable of enveloping significant areas of seabed. It can easily grow over the top of mussels and other shellfish, which may cause significant problems for sessile mollusc populations. There are also indications that scallops won't settle in areas with carpet sea squirt on them. This is, of course, not only of concern to ecologists, but to commercial shellfish growers and fishing industries, and demonstrates how easily the finely balanced marine ecosystem can be thrown out of kilter. Once introduced, it can be impossible to eradicate new species and the impacts are sometimes enormous.

I have mixed feelings about non-native species. Perhaps it's down to my own experiences of living in other countries, as I can't help but admire their determination to survive, to eke out a niche for themselves on arrival in places and in conditions that are entirely alien to them. The furthest I have ever lived from the sea was when I took up English teaching work at a university in the Colombian Andes in the third year of my modern languages degree. Although I loved everything about the place, I became aware of my habit of falling asleep facing the sea – because I now had no idea in which direction it lay. Delightful though the glossy-green humming birds and the moths as large as bats were to me, I found myself walking past the fountain in the main square one night after teaching evening classes, and gazing into the shallow pool at its foot. The reflections of the streetlamps and the sleeping colonial whitewashed walls stared back at me, but there was not so much as a goldfish living in that water. The mountain air was thin and the fog that fell over the town most evenings had no taste. By night earthquakes regularly shook the books off my shelves, and by day my time was filled with new friendships and experiences, but for all the excitement of this enchanted landscape, my craving for the sea grew in me, gradually and alarmingly, like a madness.

At the first opportunity, I travelled to the Caribbean coast with local friends, arriving on the still shores of Tolú as the sun was setting, to stand and breathe, as though experiencing oxygen for the first time. This calm sea soothed my need to reconnect for a while, but it was still a world away from the long green breakers that lined up to smash into the cliffs at home, and I thought often of the bubbling pools lined with their seaweed gardens back at my childhood beach. I visited the mangroves of the Caribbean, saw reef sharks circling bright bursts of tropical fish, swam over some sapphire-blue sea squirts guarded by a snake-like eel with needle-sharp teeth in its gaping mouth and travelled south to see the cool Pacific meeting the Peruvian desert coast. Wherever I found myself was home, but even when I began to forget words and names from my native tongue, the memories of my own shores stayed with me.

A couple of years later, while working in Brussels, blithely planning my wedding to the wrong man and still dreaming of the sea, I took up a Masters degree in environmental studies with the Open University. With seismic imprecision, my life gave a jolt in the right direction. My adventurous spirit was leading me home.

When the great taxonomist Carl Linnaeus was categorising species in the eighteenth century, he looked at the soft bodies of the sea squirts and the arrangement of their two siphons, which resemble the body plan of clams like razor shells, and concluded that these must be soft-shelled molluscs. It was a reasonable assumption: razor shells also shoot up jets of water in their rush to bury themselves when predators approach, and there are many molluscs, like sea slugs, that don't have shells.

It was around a century later that these quirky animals were definitively categorised and they were not placed with the molluscs but with the chordates; a phylum that includes reptiles, birds and us.

It was the study of plankton that uncovered the secrets of the sea squirts, just as it was with barnacles. When Polish scientist Alexander Kovalevsky observed the development of the sea squirt, he discovered something remarkable. This sessile blob starts life as a free-swimming member of the zooplankton. Far more active than its adult reproductive form, this microscopic creature looks strikingly like a tadpole. In fact, not only does it resemble a tadpole externally, the body plan and some of the internal organs are the same. It has simple eyes in the same position, a nervous cord and other similarities. In particular, it has a notochord. This primitive organ is a stiff cartilaginous rod that provides a structure to the body. In vertebrates like reptiles, amphibians, birds and mammals, the notochord developed into a backbone. However, in sea squirts this structure is lost when the animal settles and metamorphoses into its adult form. Although vertebrates and sea squirts do not have much in common in terms of their outward appearance, they are considered close relatives in biological terms. The presence of the notochord must have come as a great surprise to anyone who had ever seen these sedentary lumps of jelly.

Roll on to the twenty-first century and researchers looking at the star ascidian and a much larger squirt with striking yellow-ringed siphons, *Ciona intestinalis*, have discovered that the sea squirt's primitive heart, which is little more than a pulsing tube, contains specialist pacemaker cells much like those found in humans. These cells are able to control the rate of the sea squirt's heartbeat and even react in the same way as human cells to drugs, like cilobradine, which slow the rate of the heart. This discovery may unlock clues to how our heart evolved, and how it works.

Meanwhile another project has decoded the genome of *Ciona intestinalis*, revealing that around 80 per cent of its genes are also found in humans and other vertebrates. This project has also revealed that in other ways the sea squirts have interesting characteristics in common with plants, fungi and bacteria. For example, sea squirts create the outer casing of their tunic from a cellulose-like substance, a building material usually used only by plants. As you might expect, the cells that allow them to do this are also similar to those found in plants.

Although vertebrates, including humans, have approximately 20 times more genes in our code than a sea squirt, researchers are hoping to use the genes that we have in common to unlock further secrets about the evolutionary origin of the workings of our bodies, including our brains, eyes and immune systems. All of these things are impossible to imagine when looking at one of these mysterious sea squirts, so extremely unlike ourselves that many don't even recognise them as animals.

CHAPTER 18

Sea Slug

Back from Brussels after spending a year working in the European Commission alongside completing my Masters degree, I settled in London for another few years. Still harbouring dreams of moving back to the coast, I decided to take up rock pooling seriously. It made little sense and there was no concrete plan but, as I emerged from the wreckage of a failed marriage, the urge to reconnect with the shore had become a physical need. As though drawn by the memory of a first, idealised love, I knew that I needed to lose myself in a wilder place than Finsbury Park or Wimbledon Common. I needed a place with wide horizons and flying foam to steady my emotions and in which to pursue my own path. Undeterred by the obvious lack of rock pools where I now lived, I signed up for a series of courses at the Field Studies Council's centre at Dale Fort in Pembrokeshire, including the worm course on which I first encountered a king ragworm. Like many decisions in my life, it was based on little more than gut feeling and, like most, it worked out.

 As the train rocked past Llanelli, heading for Milford Haven, I remember leafing through my copy of the Collins *Sea Shore of Britain and Europe*, taking in the 300-odd pages of descriptions and illustrations, many of which looked unimaginably strange. After an emotionally challenging few months I planned to start with something easy. With a lifetime of shell hoarding behind me, the mollusc course seemed the obvious choice, but the fact that the molluscs section of my Collins book ran to almost 100 pages was something I only discovered on the train.

Although this guide did at least have colour pictures and provided common names where they existed, I found myself drowning in Latin. There were some anemones and crabs I recognised, some shells, then endless pages of unfamiliar creatures with all manner of tentacles and appendages. Every time I came across something I thought I knew, like the hermit crab, I would realise that there were more than half a dozen different species I might meet in the intertidal zone and I had no clue how to tell them apart. As I stared at page after page of fan worms, isopods, cephalopods and chitons, I was daunted but fascinated, already becoming hooked. This may have been the moment where the shell-collecting habit of my childhood began to morph into a more serious rock pooling addiction. I knew I was being drawn in far deeper than ever before.

Dale Fort was built to ward off Napoleonic attacks that never materialised. Its thick stone walls complete with old cannon emplacements sit tucked against a rocky headland overlooking Milford Haven on the Pembrokeshire Coast. To my eyes it was better suited to being some kind of monastery than a fort. The room was furnished comfortably but simply, yet felt like it existed only as a backdrop to my contemplation, for beyond my bedroom window was the wide, wild sea. Though I took out my identification book again, I found myself looking not at the drawings but at the long swells moving endlessly towards the coast and imagining what lay beneath their glassy surface.

We assembled in the classroom after dinner, a small group of half a dozen young people who all seemed normal enough, excepting our interest in sea shells. I quickly realised that the rest of the group was made up of conservation professionals from organisations like the National Trust and Wildlife Trusts, who routinely surveyed beaches as part of their jobs managing reserves and marine conservation strategies. I would have to work even harder to swallow the Collins book if I was going to keep up, but here was a chance to get to know people who were paid to do something I loved and hear the stories of their encounters. One of them had seen a sea slug on the nearby Llŷn Peninsula where he worked; we gathered round my book to look it up before moving on to discussing nearby pubs.

From the moment the tutor bounced into the classroom and set out the intense schedule of shore visits, lectures and laboratory sessions that would become our world that week, I was in no doubt that this was someone who not only knew his stuff but would take us further into the underwater world than I'd ever been before. His enthusiasm was infectious and, if his presentation of photos was anything to go by, I was about to meet a mind-boggling number of species. Evidently, I didn't know as much about shells as I'd thought.

The next morning I saw my first sea slug, or rather I took the tutor's word for it, because what I could see was little more than a speck on a rock.

It was a stunning speck though: vivid purple against the grey rock, a brilliant gemstone. With some persuasive prodding and sluicing with sea water, the tutor transferred the speck to a pot, ready to be transported back to the laboratory. The squidgy spot looked nothing like the illustrations in my Collins book, which had tentacles and appendages in all manner of odd geometrical shapes.

'Gather round close,' the tutor called, holding the pot in front of him, his hand poised over the lid.

We leaned in, like children at a conjuring show, waiting for the big reveal as he lifted the lid. The blob had swollen up, as though rehydrated by the sea water, stretching itself into a long, tapering oval. My first impression was of a fuzzy puff of purple; the animal was still so small that we needed hand lenses to appreciate the full detail. From nowhere, its back had inflated itself into dozens of tall, white-tipped cerata, as though the gemstone had grown into a mass of moving crystals. Longer violet tentacles spread forwards from its head, reaching out to feel their way across the pot. I was astonished, both that it was possible to notice something so small and at its sheer exoticism; it looked as though it would be more at home on a coral reef than in the chilly waters of Wales.

By the end of the second day of the course on intertidal molluscs, I had seen a vast variety of shells and slugs on the shore. My head was spinning from all the new names, and I had spent so many hours on my knees staring at molluscs with my fringe dangling in the water that, when I closed my eyes for a second, I could see slugs and snails as though they were imprinted on my eyelids. I sat up late in the lab that night, watching *Flabellina pedata*, as I knew the purple sea slug (it's now called *Edmundsella pedata*), through the eyepiece of a microscope as it slid across a Petri dish. A clutch of thick books packed with black and white line drawings and dense text describing rhinophores, mantles, cerata and propodia lay open in front of me. Apparently, the Collins book was just a starting place, and I would need to learn this whole foreign language to decipher invertebrate identification keys. I tried this for a few minutes but reverted to gazing in awe at the purple giant I could see through the eyepiece, seemingly coming straight at me with its huge tentacles held aloft, its thin tail sliding over the Perspex. Away from the camouflaging reds and browns of the seaweed, it looked more intensely purple than ever.

We had at least eight species of sea slug exploring our tank that night, awaiting their safe return to the shore the next morning. I couldn't have imagined how incredible they would be. There was a fluffy white one, a sulphurous yellow one with a dark internal shell, the bright purple one with its cerata now sticking up along its back like a Mohican, a nondescript brown one that could leach acid out of pale star-shaped pores on its back, a large white one that guzzled down an anemone in the night and turned pink, and several more besides. Every one of them was incredible in its own way. Funnily enough, despite all the glitz and display the bright-coloured slugs put on, it was the brown one that fascinated me most, partly due to its acid trick, but mostly because it had the most fabulous and memorable scientific name I have ever come across: *Discodoris planata*. To my great disappointment *Discodoris planata* was recategorised a short time later as the far less glamorous-sounding *Geitodoris planata*. I know I am not the only one who secretly carries on using the old name associated with glitter balls, flares and platform shoes on everything except official records.

By the time the course finished I was in love with sea slugs. They have continued to enchant and surprise me at every turn, and my fascination never wanes for these plucky little blobs of jelly that somehow survive extreme conditions and evade predators while displaying an incredible range of colours and body plans. When adults start rock pooling, sea slugs are often top of the list of animals they most hope to see, and sea slug groups on social media often have thousands of members. However, they can be elusive things, and it is hardly ever possible to know exactly where or when you will find them. In fact, washing out kelp holdfasts and examining flushed-out material under a microscope is likely to yield a greater number and variety of slugs than a week of searching on the shore. My preferred and highly unscientific method is to go out and look really, really closely at everything, just in case, with a particular focus on things that slugs like to eat. Most slugs have a limited diet, and many specialise in eating just a few species of sponge, sea squirt, bryozoan (also known as sea mat), anemone or hydroid (animals with stinging polyps that are related to anemones).

Although the vast majority of sea slugs are carnivores, something that sets them apart from plant-munching garden slugs, there are a few that prefer seaweed. The most spectacular of these is *Aplysia punctata*. I find it all through the winter if I look hard enough among the sparse weed that remains on the lower shore; the young slug often no more than a burgundy speck next to my fingernail, with its tiny tail visible behind a raised circle of parapodia framed in black. Two tall, rolled rhinophores sticking up from its head lend it the appearance of having tall ears. The slug's common name, sea hare, is due to these 'ears'.

Through early spring I watch the sea hares grow, swelling into brown lumps with leopard-skin patterns on their flanks and always with their tall ears standing proud as they graze their way through the early shoots of sea lettuce. Sea hares thrive among the invasive sargassum weeds that grow swiftly, choking the sea floor in a thick, slippery tangle. By early summer, the slugs have ballooned and fill my hand, collapsing into heavy blobs out of the water, but resplendently weird when in it, holding their rolled 'ears' back as they sway in the current, clinging on to seaweed and each other. Like the grazers of the plains they move in vast herds of hundreds or thousands of animals, feasting on the rich seaweed pastures and descending on the sweetest, most productive zones to breed. Their colouring blends well with the weed and at first I often miss them, despite their bulk, but as soon as I notice one, there's another close by, and another. At one public event, children were collecting them by the very heavy bucketful until I suggested the sea hares might be happier back on the seaweed. At times like this, it is impossible to move about on the shore for fear of squashing these sea slugs, and inevitably from time to time a puff of purple ink fills a pool. Like their distant relatives the squid and cuttlefish, sea hares are able to produce a cloud of ink to deter and confuse predators. It must be quite effective as few things seem to eat them.

After a few days of this mass slow-motion slug stampede, there is a change on the shore. Attached to every available piece of seaweed is a tangle of pink spaghetti. It looks like someone has spent the night spraying the shore in silly string. The twisting strings are hard to the touch and translucent. Inside each one, hundreds of eggs are developing, ready to hatch and become the tiny red specks I'll see again in winter.

Far less conspicuous, the sea hare's smaller relative, *Elysia viridis*, is another plant eater. All the books say it feeds on *Codium* sp., a green seaweed which has thick, spongey upright branches, like a tiny tree of green sausages. In fact, these slugs can be found on almost any seaweed, but they seem fond of the taste of *Codium* and these distinctive clumps are an ideal place to look. In the fifteen years since my first forays at Dale Fort I've made the journey from student to teacher. I advise groups at my workshops to search any *Codium* they find, looking for *Elysia viridis*, but it takes a leap of faith for them to believe that the black slimy smudge adorning one of the green-sausage branches is a slug. Once I have performed the magic trick of placing the slug in some water, however, it soon takes shape.

This slug only has short 'ears' compared to the sea hare, but its colouring can be far more striking with its army-green background flecked with glittering turquoise dots. Rather like the way in which the white, fluffy *Aeolidia* sp. slugs absorb reds and browns from the anemones they eat, *Elysia viridis* obtains its green colour from the seaweed it consumes. The *Elysia viridis* diet doesn't provide it with any helpful defensive stinging cells, but this incredible animal has found another way to use its food. It retains chloroplasts from the seaweed's cells and they continue to produce energy within its body, providing the slug with sugars as long as it is exposed to the sunlight. In times of food scarcity this can allow the slug to survive. In other words, the slug photosynthesises. Although relationships between some marine animals and symbiotic algae are well known, such as in snakelocks anemones which contain microscopic algae and use some of the sugars they produce, it is far rarer for an animal to appropriate a plant's chemical energy generation mechanism for its own purposes. The process is called kleptoplasty. It's a powerful thing for a centimetre-long blob to manage.

Elysia viridis, the solar-powered sea slug.

When a friend, David Fenwick, tipped me off in 2014 that the *Calma* slugs that feed on fish eggs had been split into two separate species, and sent me a detailed paper describing the new one, there was never any doubt that I would take up the challenge of trying to find some. No doubt that's why he told me. David is a remarkably knowledgeable marine recorder who has helped me out with identification and advice at every turn. He, of course, had already seen both *Calma glaucoides*, which we met in a previous chapter devouring clingfish eggs, and the new species. I am always a huge fan of sea creatures with weird names, so I was determined to meet the utterly unpronounceable *Calma gobioophaga* as soon as possible.

I set out along the coast path with my son on a mid-May morning, heading for a remote beach on Cornwall's south-east coast that I knew to be a top spot for finding fish eggs and, by default, fish-egg-eating sea slugs. As you might deduce from its name, *Calma gobioophaga* feeds on goby eggs, which shouldn't be too hard to find. However, it has mostly been observed in more southern locations along the Atlantic coast and in the Mediterranean, with the most northerly record of it at that time being David's specimen found in Hayle. This location was further north still and possibly beyond its range. A further complication was that all of the literature about this new slug suggested that it only ate the eggs of the black goby, a species that doesn't tend to lay eggs on the shore around the UK. David's specimen was almost definitely on rock goby eggs though, so I held on to hope as my son and I slid our way across to the loose rocks on a sheltered part of the shore.

Conditions were beautiful, with a calm sea running out well beyond the usual low tide mark, uncovering a plethora of glassy pools. Inevitably, we were distracted from our goby egg hunt by a clutch of light-bulb sea squirts, then an entirely white *Sagartia elegans* anemone, a writhing worm and all manner of other creatures. After half an hour of searching I still hadn't found any goby eggs, just the spherical yellow eggs of a clingfish, with no sign of any slugs attacking them. One rock did have a sulphurous yellow pair of *Berthella plumula* sea slugs happily spawning away near a patch of sponge. My son was transfixed watching them. He's always been drawn to anything dangerous: fungi, volcanoes, explosives and the like. Sea slugs that can produce a strong acid if disturbed were just what he needed to forget that it was past lunchtime. To encourage him further, I told him about the time I came home from a rock pooling session with bubbling skin on the palm of one hand, most likely caused by inadvertently disturbing a *Berthella plumula* slug as I lifted a rock. He was delighted and demanded more details.

Hunger pangs were soon setting in more forcefully, but I managed to negotiate to explore one more pool before the tide turned. My son, who knows exactly what 'just one pool' can turn into, was unconvinced, but he did like the idea of finding a goby egg-eating sea slug. Together, we identified a tight gully running into a pool with some large, loose rocks that seemed a perfect choice for any broody fish in the neighbourhood and clambered down to check them out.

We turned a couple of larger rocks and found no fish eggs. Just as my son was rightly protesting that the tide must be turning by now, I heaved up a big rock, a fish shot out from underneath and there, in the middle, was a clutch of transparent goby eggs, each shaped like a pointed capsule. We used my camera to zoom in and see that these eggs were well developed, with two black eyes staring out at us from each egg. We scanned the surface looking for slugs but disappointingly there was just a mass of greyish eggs. Nothing to see here.

Thinking that sandwiches were seconds away, my son

jumped up again and groaned to see me lifting the boulder into the water of the pool to take another look. I ignored him, as only mothers can, and adjusted the rock until all of the eggs were submerged. There was still no sign of a slug. There were, however, a few eggs in the middle that seemed a slightly darker colour than the others, an almost imperceptible break in the uniformity that I decided to investigate.

Under my camera lens the grey patch didn't look like anything special. It was a clutch of eggs that seemed more mottled, with something white in the middle. I stared for a full minute before I discerned what I thought might be a pair of tentacles or rhinophores sticking out from the eggs. Could this be a slug? I examined the grey eggs again. They were spotted with black like the fish eyes in the other eggs but these spots weren't eyes. The 'eggs' were moving towards me.

My son leaned in, wanting to know what I'd found, whether it was the slug we'd been looking for and whether it was time to eat. After a few more seconds glued to my camera, I pointed out to him the patch on my screen. I showed him the pale section in the middle, which was the slug's transparent back packed tight with white spawn ready to lay, the grey egg-like capsules either side of it that were the slug's cerata, the swaying white tentacles at the front and the round black eyes set just behind them. We squealed in excitement as it dawned on us that, for once, we'd found exactly what we'd set out to find. The slug looked steadily back at us before carrying on its way, while around it the fish eggs squirmed, twisting this way and that, the embryos inside seeing or sensing the danger, but unable to flee from the approaching predator.

I didn't dare take my eyes off that camera screen in case I lost sight of the slug. Without the help of the camera I could barely see it. It was several more minutes before I'd managed to take enough photos and video of the minute slug, and I would happily

Calma gobioophaga sea slug feeding on goby eggs.

have spent longer, but the tide was flowing in and the sandwich campaign was mounting, so I left my first *Calma gobioophaga* alone with the rock goby eggs.

There are so many things we don't yet know about sea slugs or about much of our marine wildlife. Until we look closely, we don't know what species are there, let alone how they live. The *Calma* slugs are present for a very short time each year, feeding on fish eggs for a few weeks until they hatch. Little is known about where they go for the rest of the year. Perhaps they move into deeper water and feed on other things, or perhaps they simply die, to be replaced by the babies they have spawned on the rocks where the fish lay their eggs. Either way they are seldom seen anywhere except on the fish eggs they eat.

That said, one thing we do know about *Calma glauoides* and *Calma gobioophaga* is that they have no anus. Apparently, they digest their fish-egg prey so effectively that they have no need to defecate and therefore don't require a bottom. As is often the case with marine life, the things we do know about this sea slug only add to its mysteries.

I could not have guessed when I signed up for the course at Dale Fort just how far it would take me. Somewhere between the field trips and microscopes, the banter on the minibus and just sitting in my room watching cormorants fishing off the rocks, I forgot to think of the difficult months behind me. The call of the sea had drowned out the noises, blanking them like a thick sea mist when it rolls in on a calm day.

CHAPTER 19

Catshark

February has to be one of the most challenging months on the shore, with short days, low water temperatures and brisk winds that turn my hands red and sore in minutes, and 2015 was no exception. It wasn't the ideal time to spend two days in a row on a beach but that, of course, is what I did.

The first day was a public half-term event with my amazing local Marine Conservation Group. Despite the chill factor, a score of families turned out in puffy jackets, scarves and wellies to explore the beach during an exceptional tide. We were well rewarded with a diverse haul of creatures, including several seven-armed starfish, a species which has the brightest orange arms of all our starfish, with long tube feet reaching out from underneath them. We saw scorpion fish eggs, delicate spider crabs, rocklings, sea lemon slugs and even a lozenge-shaped pink blob that required several days and the help of an expert forum to identify as a type of sea cucumber, or part of one at least.

Towards the end of the session, which we were cutting short so that we didn't lose anyone to hypothermia, a friend who had brought her hardy children along called me over. She was striding out of a pool at the edge of the lower shore, her hair tousled and her cheeks burning red with cold, bucket held aloft like a triumphant Boudica of the rock pools. Four excited children bounced alongside her, splashing and waving their hands. Together we crouched, placing the bucket on the rocks between us and peered in.

'I just saw it and scooped it in,' she said, as wide-eyed as the children. 'I've never found one before.'

My eyes were no less huge. Lying perfectly still in the bottom of the bucket, its tail curled around its head, watching us warily through narrow green eyes, was a shark. It was just a baby, probably a newborn that had emerged from its egg case in the last few days. The dark stripes on its body made it hard to miss against the sides of the bucket, but would allow it to disappear among the kelp fronds. Already bigger than some rock pool fish at around half a ruler's length, this hatchling would reach around 160 centimetres as an adult, which is close to my height. Whether you know it as the greater spotted catshark, greater spotted dogfish, bull huss, nursehound, flake or rigg; the *Scyliorhinus stellaris* is an impressive fish. Needless to say, the baby shark drew quite a crowd of awestruck children before my friend released it back where she found it.

There are around ten species of shark that are regularly found in UK inshore waters, but only two of them are likely to turn up in the rock pools. The lesser spotted catshark, often called the lesser spotted dogfish or small spotted catshark, is the smaller and more common of the two and adults of this species are occasionally found stranded in the pools on the biggest tides. The other species, the greater spotted catsharks, like the baby shark my friend scooped up in her bucket, are less commonly seen but do come inshore to lay their eggs, congregating in particular nursery areas to lay their rectangular yellow capsules in shallow water. The

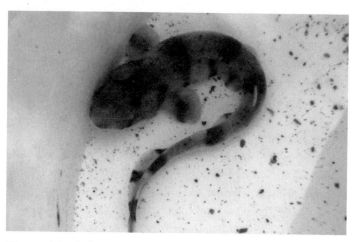

The recently hatched greater spotted catshark *Scyliorhinus stellaris* in a bucket before being released.

female catshark positions herself, usually against clumps of the rainbow weed *Cystoseira tamariscifolia* or other seaweeds of this genus, laying two egg cases at a time, one from each ovary, onto the sturdy branches of the seaweed, where they attach firmly by means of their curly tendrils which are located at either end of the capsule. They then remain in place for many months, resisting the forces of the currents, tides and storms.

Much is still unknown about the lives of greater spotted catsharks. Some important nursery sites have been identified but it is likely that there are others that remain undiscovered. The conditions that affect how long the egg cases take to hatch are also unknown but the length of gestation seems to vary between sites and regions. At one site I visit regularly there are sometimes dozens of baby catsharks lurking close to their empty egg cases, suggesting that they have hatched at about the same time, perhaps coinciding with particularly large spring tides. Fresh cases appear at all times of year, smooth and shining pale against

Catshark egg case.

the darker weeds. Inside, a fat round yolk rests in the lower half of the case.

As each case matures it seems to darken as it loses its translucency. When held to the light, the silhouette of an active baby shark appears, wriggling and developing its swimming muscles in the safety of its protective case, still fed by the diminishing yolk.

Like any other new surface in the marine environment, over time the egg cases are colonised by a colourful array of seaweeds and animals. Pink encrusting seaweeds, white tube worms, tufty red seaweeds and yellow, blue and purple star ascidian sea squirts all move in. By the time the baby catshark has reached maturity and squeezed its way out of the end of the case, its former home is indistinguishable from the seaweed around it, perfectly camouflaged in its cloak of life forms. The process takes around seven to nine months and the young shark that emerges from the case is fully formed and ready to fend for itself, although it will not be a mature adult for about another four years.

The spent egg cases of the catsharks and their relatives the rays, which lay their eggs in deeper water, frequently wash up on beaches. As a child I simply knew them as mermaids' purses and I especially prized the glossy black egg cases of the cuckoo ray with their long curving horns at each corner, but now I collect them for a different reason. Once they have been soaked overnight, it is possible to measure them and observe their shape to work out exactly which species laid the egg case. The Shark Trust have been collecting data through their Great Eggcase Hunt since 2003, amassing a wealth of information which is helping to build up a picture of the health of the shark and ray populations around the UK. Anyone can submit data to this popular citizen science project using a simple identification key and online form. Over 100,000 records have been sent in so far.

Sharks and rays, which all have a cartilaginous skeleton, tend to have a slow breeding rate and take a number of years to reach maturity. Some species are especially vulnerable to overfishing and the nurseries where they lay their egg cases can also be destroyed by trawling gear. Even the greater spotted catshark is fished and appears on some fish shop menus as 'rock salmon', which is an amalgam term for a range of species. There are increasing concerns that some of our shark species may be targeted illegally for the shark fin trade. Catsharks are unlikely to be targeted for their fins but are frequently caught by bottom-trawling gear and are mostly discarded, with varying survival rates. Consequently, dead catsharks are a depressingly common sight on our shores.

The largest of our rays, the common skate, *Dipturus intermedia*, now known as the flapper skate, used to be a common sight in fishmongers around Europe. It lays a humungous egg case measuring up to 20 centimetres long. A second species, the blue skate, *Dipturus flossada*, was also previously known as common skate, but is a little smaller and seems to have a more southerly distribution. It takes the flapper skate around 11 years to reach maturity and begin to breed, by which time it is usually at least 1.5 metres from 'wingtip to wingtip'. This slow reproduction rate leaves it extremely vulnerable to overfishing and it has been fished to near extinction in most UK waters. Although there is now a ban on targeted commercial fishing for both species of the common skate all around the UK, with some additional restrictions in place in Scotland and Northern Ireland, any recovery in skate numbers will take an extremely long time, if it comes at all. I keep looking but I have never found a blue skate egg case on the tideline.

The day after the public rock pooling event, I couldn't help myself. I wondered if there might be more catshark hatchlings about and decided to risk chilblains by exploring the shore a second time, accompanied by Ed and Junior.

The day was as still as I could hope for but the icy breaths of easterly wind that pushed white clouds along the coast were freezing the tips of my ears, nose, fingers and toes. The process was gradual but steady.

The joy and frustration of rock pooling is never knowing what you are going to find. It is impossible to know whether, if you stay five more minutes, you might discover something incredible, or if you'll find nothing and get even colder.

The first hour or so of rooting about in the pools yielded bright dahlia anemones, small spider crabs festooned in seaweeds and sponges, and a hungry spiny starfish chomping on a dog whelk. By this time the tide had dropped far enough to allow me to wade across a ridge of loose stones to a rocky outcrop covered in a living collage of sponges and sea squirts, while Ed and Junior remained behind among the sheltered lower shore gullies. I knelt at the water's edge to photograph a sea cucumber, taking breaks to plunge my hands inside my scarf to warm them, waiting for the searing pain to pass as my fingers reheated before grabbing my camera and setting to work again. I hadn't brought a notebook to the beach and would have been incapable of grasping a pencil when I was this cold, so I tried to take a photo of every species that I wanted to record.

Soon, despite the protection of my waders and layers, I could feel cold setting in more deeply and knew it was time to give up for the day before my brain followed my hands' example and seized up. I turned to begin the long sloosh back across the lagoon, taking care not to slip and fill my waders.

I had only covered a few metres and was still a long way out from the rocks of the lower shore, with no one else in sight, when a distant movement caught my eye. A patch of kelp maybe 50 metres from where I was standing was jerking and swaying, sending out rippling waves in all directions around it. There are several shallow patches of water that form between the raised rocky ridges around the lagoon, and it's not unusual for shoals of fish to become trapped by the tide and to thrash around in their search for an exit. I had no binoculars with me, so did my best to focus my cold-addled brain and watering eyes on the swirling kelp to see if I could make anything out.

Whatever fish were causing the disturbance, they looked too big to be mackerel. Mullet and bass went through my mind, but as I watched the churning water, it took shape and broke away from the kelp to swim towards me. As one, with a single thrashing tail, dorsal fins set well back and a wide, blunt head that jerked from side to side as it swam, the fish wrestled its way through the tangles of kelp and weed, fighting its way straight towards me. Unmistakeably, it was a shark.

This was by far the largest catshark I had ever seen, probably because all of the others had been either baby greater spotted catsharks or adult small spotted catsharks, which only reach around 75 centimetres in length. At moments like this, the wide peaceful water takes on a more hostile aspect. My subconscious unhelpfully began retrieving images of mediaeval illustrations of sea monsters, giant squid and serpents. Why, it wondered, had I ever thought it a good idea to wander about the edge of the ocean armed only with rubber waders to protect me from the wild beasts? On the other hand my conscious brain was certain that it had read somewhere that catsharks were passive creatures that only ever bit when handled, so I had better stop worrying and start trying to film it. My cold, shaky hands were going to demand all of my concentration to manage any passable photos or videos. I did my best to track the catshark's progress through the lagoon, keeping it in my viewfinder as it dived and surfaced, weaving left and right and looming ever larger.

I didn't dare move. The shark was coming in my direction and it was now a few seconds from reaching me. My greatest fear was not being bitten, or rather not the bite itself, but the fear that it might pierce my waders and let the icy water in.

I did my best to look like seaweed.

A moment later, the catshark glided in alongside me and touched down less than a metre from me on the gravelly sea floor, where the water was deep enough to cover all but the rounded top of its back. The world seemed to hang in suspension and I almost stopped breathing for a moment, waiting to see what the shark would do next.

It did nothing.

Looking settled, almost sleepy, the catshark lay perfectly still. I realised it may have heard the splashing of my boots and come to investigate, probably expecting to find another catshark here.

At such close quarters it ought to have been possible to make a definite identification, and from the size alone and its broad body I was sure that this must be the larger of the two catshark species, the greater spotted catshark. The pattern of spots is especially variable in the greater spotted catshark and can be anything from small spots and splodges, to leopard spots, to being almost entirely black. The main identification feature in these two fish, other than their size, is the arrangement of their nasal flaps. In other words, I would need a good photo of the underside of the fish's head to see whether or not those white flaps of skin were fused to the mouth. No matter how non-aggressive this species might be, there was no way I was going to risk putting my hand in the water in front of its mouth. Apart from that, my hands were at their limit of cold and I couldn't bear the idea of putting them back in the water.

Had I touched the shark, I would have found that its smooth-looking skin is made up of densely packed teeth-like scales, which all lie in one direction and reduce friction as the shark moves through the water, making it hydrodynamic but extremely rough to touch against the grain. Fishermen around here used to dry the skins of catsharks to use as sandpaper. Unsurprisingly, catsharks can do quite some damage to bare arms if they don't want to be held. J. Couch's, *A History of the Fishes of the British Isles*, published in 1862, warns that the catshark uses its skin as a secret weapon:

> When seized it throws its body round the arm that holds it, and by a contractile and reversed action of its body grates over the surface of its enemy with the rugged spines of its skin, like a rasp. There are few animals that can bear so severe an infliction, by which their surface is torn with lacerated wounds.

Although this has the ring of a Victorian cautionary tale and most catsharks are docile when handled, I wasn't going to take chances, especially on this remote beach. I made do with taking photos from where I was standing, a solution far from adequate to show the size of the fish or any of its definitive features, but nonetheless effective in proving to others afterwards that I really had stood next to a shark.

The tide was due to turn and the shark was comfortable where it was, so I inched my feet backwards, putting some distance between us before I dared turn and walk away, checking over my shoulder that it wasn't following me, without a clue what to do if it was.

Perhaps the strangest thing about such encounters on the shore is that, despite the intensity of the experience, the emotions and the excitement, the whole thing often passes in lonely silence. Only when I had crossed the whole slippery lagoon, traced my way through a long gully among the lower shore rocks and clambered up onto the middle shore, did I finally rejoin my family, who had been looking for fish in the shallow pools, and blurt out through chattering teeth, 'I saw a shark!'

The catshark that swam towards me and settled near my feet.

CHAPTER 20

Squat Lobster

The single triangular fin of a porpoise rose and fell among jostling sets of waves a couple of hundred metres from the starboard bow of the MS *Oldenburg*, its progress followed by dozens of pairs of binoculars including my own. As it turned away from the boat, cutting across the current between the English mainland and the Welsh coast, a second, smaller fin was revealed, sheltering behind its mother's body, visible for a few moments before both melted into the churning sea. The early September air, still fresh as a spring day, shepherded fluffy clouds northwards, clearing the view of the distant mound of Lundy that at first was no more than a molehill on the horizon.

Our visit was a last-minute decision to flee London for a weekend, something my partner, Ed, and I were doing with increasing frequency as we began to imagine a life together. Thanks to the Masters degree and a timely opportunity, I had been working for Friends of the Earth for several years now in a job I adored, but I sensed that this was the time to leave the city, as I had always known I would. Our plan was to edge south-westwards from London, find a house and start a family somewhere greener and closer to the sea, although it was proving difficult to imagine a way back to Cornwall, where we had both grown up. Our shared memories of our own Cornish childhoods were of wide spaces and salt air, but with soaring second home ownership pushing the prices skywards and a hopeless lack of year-round employment, the villages we grew up in were beyond our reach. Lucky in so many other ways, we accepted for now that our coastal fixes would have to come in small doses, and few places are better for a quick marine hit than Lundy.

As we approached, the island swelled into a towering rock, surrounded by a swarm of black dots. With the nesting season coming to a close many birds had already left on their travels, and those remaining would soon be dispersing to live the rest of the year at sea. Ours would be one of the last boats of the year to be piloted into the landing bay by a tight flock of puffins, scudding across the water before us and arcing away towards the towering cliffs.

Lundy's location and geology are something of an anomaly. Its rounded bulk stands far from any other land and is made from the same granite as is found in parts of Northern Ireland and the Western Isles of Scotland; a granite of a completely different and younger type from that found in Dartmoor. This mound of magma cooled slowly beneath the surface of the ground many millions of years ago, attaching itself to a mass of hard slate, which now forms a towering cliff alongside the quay. In places, the magma intruded into the sedimentary rocks, leading to the formation of the deep caves and underwater walls of rock that now abound with life.

The wide range of seashore and seabed habitats make Lundy a hotbed of marine wildlife and a favourite with divers, but through the 1960s and early 1970s, as diving increased, the removal of crayfish and other animals such as sea fans that were kept or sold as souvenirs became a serious concern for local conservationists. A group of divers first raised the 'need for underwater conservation' in the UK in a letter to the Natural Environment Research Council (NERC) in 1965. They suggested the creation of marine reserves at Skomer, St Anthony's Head and the Farne Islands and Holy Island, but Lundy was not on their proposed list. Members of Ilfracombe and North Devon Sub Aqua Club published an article in 1969 on setting up UK marine reserves and, following an evidence gathering mission, club member Heather Machin followed this up with a specific proposal for Lundy.

When the island was taken over by the Landmark Trust later that year, marine ecologist, conservationist and keen diver Keith Hiscock worked with the new owners and the users of the island and its waters to put in place a management strategy for the new reserve. Lundy became a Voluntary Marine Nature Reserve in 1971 and the scheme was so successful that it was reproduced in several other places, including St Abbs on the Berwickshire coast and Skomer Island off the coast of Pembrokeshire. Lundy's value was officially recognised in 1986, when it became the first statutory Marine Nature Reserve in Britain, a move that paved the way for the current wave of national marine park designations. Lundy was the first Marine Conservation Zone in the UK to be declared in 2010 and is now part of a growing number of Marine Protected Areas. A no-take zone first established in 2003 also helps to protect the island from over-fishing and damage to sensitive habitats. Although the island's waters are best known by divers, its intertidal habitats are also protected, and with good reason.

The MS *Oldenburg* docked on a spring tide that was falling fast to reveal a beach strewn with mixed granite and slates, ideal for sheltering rock pool animals. It was clear why the quay was built on this part of the island. In every direction around us steep rocks rose from the sea, making the coasts inaccessible and treacherous.

Not many people seemed to visit the beach, despite its proximity to the quay, with most visitors wanting to walk around the cliff paths, see the sea birds and visit the Marisco Tavern. Being a rock pooler often means clambering up and down steep paths, so it was a welcome turn of events to watch others lumbering up the precipitous zigzag path forming a diminishing trail of colourful dots, while my partner and I stepped onto the shore to explore the peaceful bay.

There is something especially rewarding about visiting a wild place within an area that is already remote. Watching the ship, our only link to the mainland, lurching on its mooring added to the sense of peace and precariousness.

It came as no surprise that this shore was rich and diverse. Among the midshore stones were beadlet anemones in traffic light colours from bright red to vivid green. We struck out for the lower shore, looking at sponges and seaweeds on the way. Beneath the first rock was a *Xantho pilipes* crab, its brutishly thick-set claws raised towards us, its hairy back legs splayed behind its marbled brown shell. On another rock a male long-clawed porcelain crab put on a similar display of force, despite being small enough to sit comfortably in the middle of my palm. The crab somehow defied gravity, raising its swollen right claw, which measured several times the length of its own body, without keeling over. We left it clinging to the bottom of a rock.

It was our next find that made me gasp with excitement. When I moved a rock I glimpsed the long lobster-like claws and imagined for a second that it might be a baby lobster, until I realised that the muddy, chestnut colour was all wrong. Whatever it was, it was propelling itself backwards away from me faster than I could focus on it. I engaged in an ungainly pursuit through the pools, grabbing at the fleeing animal and missing, partly from fear of hurting it and partly from hopelessly bad coordination, until I was able to corner it and scoop it into my hand for a closer look.

Only a few centimetres long, even when its outsize long claws were included, this *Galathea squamifera* squat lobster was still a magnificent beast. Despite their superficial resemblance to a lobster, the squat lobsters are a separate family, most easily recognised by their lack of a long tail. Each claw, easily longer than the rest of the animal's body, was fringed in long, sharp spines and terminated in an elongated, white-tipped set of pincers. Nestled between the claws and adding to the creature's armoured appearance was the spiky rostrum sticking out, nose-like, between two beady black eyes, followed by the layered armour plates of its back, all in the same dark sheen.

Squat lobsters are common around most of the coasts of north-west Europe, but few casual rock poolers will ever see one as they are creatures of the extreme low water and are experts in shooting away to hide among the rocks and seaweed, never to be seen again. Turning this one over in my palm, which was harder

A common squat lobster, *Galathea squamifera*.

than it sounds, revealed what makes these crustaceans such effective escape artists.

Tucked under the squat lobster's abdomen was a widely rounded tail flap, not dissimilar to the tail of a female crab. Just like the crabs, the female squat lobster keeps her ruby-red treasure trove of ripening eggs under this tail. On close inspection, the flap is far thinner and more manoeuvrable than a crab's tail, and its scalloped edge is densely fringed with thin hairs. This allows the squat lobster to use it as a paddle, flapping its tail rapidly to pull itself backwards through the water at great speed. As I held the squat lobster in an awkward upside-down position, it did a demonstration of this skill, fluttering its tail and writhing, so I released it quickly back into the pool.

Later, from a high clifftop, we watched the tide rising and flowing into the sheltered pools beneath the eastern cliffs of the island, while grey seals bobbed in the water with whiskered noses lifted to the clear sky. From up here all looked calm, but even with its legal protection and conservation measures, the island's wildlife was facing unseen threats.

The name Lundy is thought to come from the Norse for puffin island, suggesting that these iconic birds have always thrived here. But in 2005 the breeding population on Lundy was down to just a few pairs and there was a real danger that they would soon be wiped out altogether. Puffins borrow rabbit burrows to nest in and leave their chicks safely tucked away while they go off to fish. This leaves the chicks well protected against aerial attacks from great black-backed gulls, but it is no use at all against the rats which at some point had been accidentally introduced to the island. From 2003 a rat-culling programme began, which continued until the island was declared rat-free. The recovery of the puffins and other ground-nesting birds, such as the Manx shearwater, was meteoric. By 2017 puffin numbers had risen from 5 to 375 birds and 80 chicks fledged from 130 nesting burrows, while the number of Manx shearwater exploded from around 300 before the cull to 3,451 nesting pairs in 2013.

Although culling any wild animal is not a decision to be taken lightly, the rat cull shows that removing a destructive introduced species can help to restore the ecological balance of a place, and similar culls have been successful on other islands. Whether the population of puffins recovers to the levels recorded in the early twentieth century of about 3,500 birds will depend on continued rat control, but also on many other things, such as disturbance from visitors, marine pollution, climate and the availability of food, especially sand eels. When it comes to sea birds, protecting the marine environment on which they depend is just as important as protecting their nesting sites. Puffins roam far and wide during their adult life, so although Lundy provides a safe nesting place, their welfare is far from guaranteed.

A couple of years after our trip to Lundy, when life had shifted once again with the arrival of our son, the call of the sea finally won us over. With far more ease than we had imagined, we were able to move close to where my partner grew up on the sheltered south coast of Cornwall thanks to an unexpected job opportunity for Ed in Plymouth. We slipped into a new closeness with the shores and with family and our two-year-old son adjusted happily to spending his days on the beach. Although our home villages were out of our price bracket, our local beaches in Looe offered perfect conditions for squat lobsters. Before we had even moved into our new house, I became involved with the vibrant local network of marine groups and naturalists with whom I have now shared many encounters. Since our move the marine world has infiltrated all of our lives and become my work; and yet it seems that the more I know, the more I discover and learn.

In an especially deep rocky overhang lined with turquoise gem anemones near my home, I now often see another member of the squat lobster family, *Galathea strigosa*. It is distinguished by the bright blue lines on its carapace, including a blue mask around its eyes, red stripes on its legs and red-tipped spines between its eyes and on its claw-tips, colours similar to those on a puffin's summer beak. Unlike the puffin, the squat lobster spends the whole year in these rainbow colours instead of losing them each autumn.

There are still more species of squat lobster that usually live too far offshore for the rock pooler to find. During a children's event in west Cornwall, I found a one-centimetre-long squat lobster, which I assumed to be a baby *Galathea squamifera*. To my delight it moulted in the shore laboratory tray right in front of our eyes – although due to its minuscule size we could only see it properly through my camera's magnification. It stepped backwards out of its entire shell leaving behind an exact, empty replica of itself. I wish I had found a way to keep the moult, especially as after the event, aided by the wonders of social media, I discovered that this tiny squat lobster with blue and white claws and a pale stripe on its back was very much like a species called *Galathea intermedia*, which is usually only seen by divers. Should I ever find another one I'll know to look for the five blue spots under its chin, but at the time I had no idea.

Compared to the squat lobsters, lobsters, *Homarus gammarus*, are titans, with the largest recorded specimen weighing over 40 kilograms and measuring over 1 metre. I have no idea what I would do if I were to meet one that size in a rock pool, as I have always found even an average-sized one quite intimidating. Fortunately for me, lobsters in the wild spend most of the daytime tucked away in a safe spot deep under the rocks, emerging only at night to roam the seabed in search of food. Female lobsters will also wander searching for the largest male lobster in their area when they are ready to moult and mate. When she finds the right candidate, she hangs around outside his burrow squirting urine out of her head to fill his den with her special 'perfume' until he comes out to meet her.

In the daytime it is possible to find a lobster lurking in its burrow. There is one that sometimes resides in the same deep overhang as the colourful *Galathea strigosa* squat lobster on my local beach. It's small and unintimidating but still has a substantial crushing claw.

On a regular return visit to my childhood rock pooling beach, under an hour away from my new home, I received one of the biggest shocks I've ever had in the rock pools.

There's always an element of danger on wild Atlantic-facing beaches. The waves crash over the rocks even on calm days. I scrambled between the cliffs and a rocky outcrop, jumped across some pools that would go over my head if I slipped into their icy green waters and pressed on until I could go no further down the deep wave-cut gully. Foaming seas boomed through hidden rock tunnels nearby and the pool by my feet made odd squelchings and gurglings as the swell filled and drained it from some unseen source. Keeping a watchful eye on the restless sea, I explored the colourful turf of animals living on the rock face.

Among the young barnacle spats, colonies of sea squirts and bright sponges I noticed a small sea slug that I wanted to look at more closely. I eased myself across the rock until I was crouching at the edge of the pool, propping myself against the rough barnacles on the opposite rock, holding a pot of sea water ready as I coaxed the slug from the rock. Once I had my slug in water, I sat on the poolside, dangling my feet into the water and placed the pot on a level patch of rock beside me to watch the slug unfurl.

As I adjusted my camera settings I froze, aware of a movement at the periphery of my vision. I wasn't sure what was down there in the water below my feet but it was big enough that I instinctively swung my camera up into position. From beneath a hidden shelf of rock, at the bottom of the deep pool, two dark claws the length of my forearm were sliding forwards. The one nearest me was muscular looking and was held slightly open as though ready to demonstrate its bone-crushing abilities. The other, more slender claw sported a line of white spots. Tapering red antennae swept the sand in front of the lobster's bulbous black eyes as its head appeared, followed by a much smaller, cobalt blue pair of legs tipped in yellow pincers. I hadn't noticed before that lobsters had two pairs of claws. Still seeming to drift forward in slow motion came several more pairs of blue legs.

Doing my best not to disturb the water, I drew my feet up, curling my toes inside my beach shoes, suddenly aware of how alone I was in this hidden gully, perched on a rock, being watched by this lobster. Caught between vulnerability and the overwhelming excitement of meeting such an impressive lobster in the intertidal zone, I overcame my trepidation and focused my efforts on breathing normally and fumbling with my camera without dropping it or myself into the pool.

For a few seconds the lobster and I stared each other out, probably both equally surprised by the other's presence. Then, as smoothly and slowly as it had appeared, the lobster slipped back into its cave.

Sadly, many people see lobsters as something for the pot, so I take care never to reveal the exact location of those I find on the shore. On average, lobsters can live for around 30 to 50 years,

I almost dropped my camera when this lobster emerged from under an overhang.

the females being longer-lived than the males. However, some exceptionally large lobsters have been found that are believed to be over a century old, although it is impossible to know for sure. Their longevity is probably aided by the presence of an enzyme called telomerase in the lobsters' cells, which repairs strands of DNA known as telomeres, preventing the deterioration usually associated with ageing. Lobsters don't begin breeding until they are around five years old, so careful conservation efforts are important to ensure that they are not fished before they reach maturity. Given the difficulty of accessing the places they inhabit, even on a good spring tide, most lobsters that make their homes on the lower shore are probably safe enough, perhaps safer than those that live in waters more accessible to fishing boats and divers.

I returned to that same pool a few months later, holding my son's hand as much to keep myself upright as to help him as we slipped and climbed over the rocks. We waited for half an hour for Bob the Lobster, as he was now known, to show himself, but there was no movement in the dark cave. Perhaps we were too noisy or perhaps Bob had moved on, but more likely he is still lurking under that overhang, staying out of sight of both predators and prey. Perhaps if we had dared to dangle our feet into the water he might have been tempted out, but we preferred to keep clear. We continue to return, on the rare occasions when the conditions allow us, to Bob's home to watch and wait.

CHAPTER 21

Pipefish

While the summer holidaymakers were still sleeping in their beds or having an early breakfast, the three of us set out on our family expedition from Looe through the open meadow, seen only by a small dot of a skylark, which sang its tumbling song high above the hillside. Across the water, the horizon opened out along a quiet sea, while calling oystercatchers scooted over the surface of the waves, almost dipping their wingtips as they raced us to the pools. Newly hatched red admiral butterflies posed on the sloe bushes, airing their perfect wings on the warming breeze and shimmering under an eager sun.

We climbed the ever-narrowing coastal path, scaling the cliffs until the beach was a dizzying sheer drop below us, last winter's landslips still visible in the graded colours of the rocks. Carrying our precious picnic and a jumble of beach shoes, towels and tubs, we descended a winding path to one of our many summer getaway beaches, where my son, aged seven at the time, could swim in his favourite pool and my other half could sleep and snorkel while I made the most of the low tide before lunch.

Apart from a pair of ravens circling overhead and a heron standing stock still in a pool, its head cocked waiting for a fish to move, we had the beach to ourselves. My son and I slipped on our swimmers and beach shoes and paddled together in the cool waters of his pool, watching shore crabs, prawns and anemones until it was time for me to follow the receding tide, enjoying the gentle lapping of the water at my feet, then my ankles, knees and waist, as I explored ever deeper into a rocky gully leading out to the sea. Unencumbered by wellies or waders, there seemed to be no limit to how far I could go.

As I lowered myself further into the pool to look for sponges, slugs and the like, I became increasingly aware of how thick the kelp was, how slippery it made the unseen rocks underfoot and how suitable this place was for catsharks, which often choose to rest at the bottom of gullies. I was completely hidden from sight behind the towering rocks and up to my chest in the water now, and there could easily be jellyfish lurking between the kelp fronds. This was probably a good time to retreat a little and find a safer area to investigate.

I turned to find a foothold but saw something move among the weed. It was small, thank goodness, and thin. A worm of some sort I thought, undulating and twisting as it swam. Something else brushed my leg, but I told myself it was just weed. As I looked, I saw another worm-like thing and another. Thread-like and delicate, the swimming things were all around me, disappearing under the kelp and emerging, not seeming to have any direction or organisation to their endeavours.

After a few failed attempts, I managed to scoop one of these odd worms into a tub. What I saw was so unexpected that I forgot where I was, lost my footing and almost went under the kelp, thinking only of holding the tub aloft so as not to lose the creature as my feet scrambled against the weed.

I regained my balance in an unseemly style and looked again to check. The animal had a long, trumpeted snout, in front of wide eyes and a domed head, just like a seahorse. The head merged into a long, snaking body tipped with a fanned tail fin. From the straight sides of the body it was clear that this was no seahorse, although it was a close relative of one. I had seen plenty of pipefish before but the miniscule size and pale, yellow colour of this one were entirely new to me. I took some photos, which wasn't an easy task with the fish wriggling constantly, curling its nose right into its tail and flicking away again, but I didn't try to hold it for fear of hurting it.

I soon realised that this pipefish with its long fine nose and ridged sides, which gave its body a hexagonal cross-section, must be a greater pipefish, a fish that reaches around half a metre long when fully grown. This one and all the others in the pool were more like two centimetres. Most incredible of all, each fish had a bright yellow pouch under its belly. These fish had to be babies and the yellow sac was the remains of the egg. These greater pipefish babies had hatched very recently, quite possibly in this very pool.

Wondering if what I had felt against my leg might have been an adult pipefish, I searched among the kelp but, of course, found

A just-hatched greater pipefish.

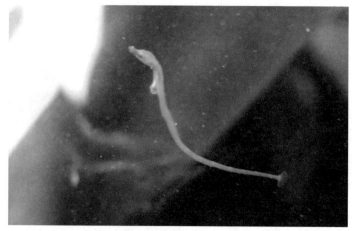

nothing. Pipefish are so well camouflaged among the seaweed that their main defence when threatened is to float, completely still, rendering them almost invisible to any predators. In this tangled pool it would be impossible to find the parent pipefish even if it were still there.

In all pipefish, it is the male, not the female, that gives birth to the babies, just as it is in seahorses. When pipefish mate, the female passes her eggs over to the male's brood pouch where they stay until they hatch. Unlike some other pipefish this species is not monogamous, so the male pipefish may store the eggs of several different females in his capacious pouch until they are ready to hatch out, usually giving birth to dozens of babies at a time.

Pipefish births are sometimes filmed in aquaria, but only very rarely in the wild, and babies this size are not often seen. Had I realised, I would have taken more photos, but instead I made do with a few shots before releasing the baby back into the pool, where it looped and twisted away beneath the kelp and was gone.

There are six species of pipefish in our waters, and two species of their close cousins, the seahorses, all of which share a similar equine profile. On the shore by far the most common species is the worm pipefish, *Nerophis lumbriciformis*, which despite being less than half the length of the greater pipefish and far more petite, is just as captivating.

Like their larger cousins, worm pipefish are equipped with intricate marbled patterns or stripes that break up their outline, together with a strong resemblance to strands of seaweed. They vary from red to green to brown, but all are within the palette of the intertidal algae to ensure good camouflage. It's not unusual to lift a rock and find a pile of worm pipefish, twisted and interlaced together, unmoving and limp as a pile of seaweed and very often entwined with thong weed or bladderwrack. Their trick is convincing. Unless you suspect they are there and actively look for the thin shapes of their bodies and the tapering of their tails, you will often not notice them.

Unlike the greater pipefish though, the worm pipefish is thought to be monogamous, choosing a mate and staying together for life. Although this is hard to verify in the field, I regularly find pipefish couples with their tails looped around one another like love knots, anchoring each other against currents and predators. The thought of separating life-long mates horrifies me, so I prefer to leave pipefish where I find them and encourage others to do the same. I always wonder, on the occasions people unwittingly pick worm pipefish up and carry them off in a bucket, whether they will find their mate again if they are released on some foreign part of the shore.

Although I have never seen worm pipefish hatching, let alone a newborn baby of this species, it is easy at almost any time of year to find a male that is 'pregnant' with developing eggs. Instead of a brood pouch, the male worm pipefish sports a deep groove on his underside, along either side of which the fertilised eggs, passed to him by the female for safekeeping, are neatly arranged in two straight lines. When the eggs are well developed, it's possible to see the babies' big eyes inside. In the adult pipefish those eyes are one of the most extraordinary things to watch. They have contortionist powers, swivelling forward and back and also up and down. Strangest of all is when each eye moves independently to look in a different direction. This impressive display gives the pipefish 360-degree vision, allowing them to spot prey and predators in all directions.

Picture a meadow of waving grass where tall green fronds sway, lush and rich. On land, this is a familiar sight, but in some places the seabed is also transformed into a pasture by seagrass. Eel grass, sweet sea grass, sedge, marlee, slitch, wigeon grass or, in Irish and Scottish Gaelic, *bilearach*; different names abound marking how special and widespread these plants are. Whether in patches or large areas, seagrass can be found in scattered locations from the Isles of Scilly and Channel Islands to Orkney and Shetland and many places in-between, as well as on many other northern European coasts. *Zostera marina* is the most common species, although two other species, the dwarf eelgrass, *Zostera noltei*, and the beaked tasselweed, *Ruppia maritima*, are also found in some locations. These 'grasses' are the only fully marine flowering plants, although their flowers will certainly never grace a vase, being little more than curling hairs on the leaves. Seagrasses are not algae and have little in common with seaweeds, which do not have roots or flowers, but like all plants they need access to sunlight to photosynthesise. Consequently, they grow only in the first ten metres or so of water, including the lower shore. During the lowest tides, some seagrass beds may be completely exposed.

Beneath the seabed, brown, lumpy rhizomes spread and tangle, holding the seagrass fast against strong currents and tides and spreading, putting up new, cloned shoots as they go. This method of growth means that individual seagrass plants constantly renew themselves and as a consequence can live for incredibly long periods. DNA studies on some Mediterranean seagrasses have shown that they have been alive for tens or even hundreds of thousands of years.

During their lives, the spreading rhizome system of seagrasses fixes sediment in place where it would otherwise be washed away, retaining nutrients and providing an effective barrier against storm damage. Where there is a seagrass bed, the water is clearer, with slowing currents dropping sediment that is then trapped and stabilised, improving water quality and helping oxygenate it.

Just as pastures provide important habitats, seagrass meadows also offer shelter to all sorts of marine animals. Currents are slowed by seagrass meadows, allowing mobile sediment to settle and be trapped among the rhizomes, providing a habitat for a diversity of species. They are nurseries for young fish, including many commercial species. Anemones, hydroids and other animals attach to them, cuttlefish hunt in them, crabs and prawns lurk among them and molluscs and worms enjoy wallowing in the stable sediments. They are also a known habitat of seahorses and pipefish, although these enigmatic fish are found on a range of seaweeds and much is unknown about their range.

Seagrasses are extremely sensitive to the addition of nutrients from sewage or agricultural run-off and can also be affected by disease. Large areas of our seagrass beds were lost due to such problems in the 1920s and 30s and have never recovered. Coastal development, trampling, dredging and trawling, among other things, threaten seagrass in the UK and worldwide, with around 7 per cent of the world's known seagrass beds being lost each year.

Loss of seagrass reduces coastal protection and, as seagrass is an effective absorber of carbon dioxide, can contribute to climate change. Seagrass has an official UK Biodiversity Action Plan and its inclusion in the designations of Marine Protected Areas and other conservation areas in the UK aims to prevent damage to these important beds. Seahorses too are protected species but in reality seagrass beds are suffering, including those in seahorse strongholds like Studland Bay in Dorset. Boat anchors of the many pleasure boats that use the bay in summer drag and scour the seagrass bed, and pollution is also causing diebacks, but conservationists' efforts to address these issues have met with resistance from those who favour short-term commercial and economic interests. In 2008 a dive survey found about 40 spiny seahorses in Studland Bay but by 2018 none were found. Although it is impossible to say for sure whether this apparent decline is entirely due to deterioration in the condition of the habitat, doing nothing to address the obvious threats to marine life cannot be right.

Marine habitats are out of sight for most people, but failing to recognise their value or the true impact of our activities can lead to irreversible loss of species, coastal protection and fish stocks. Projects by the Community Seagrass Initiative, The Wildlife Trusts and other conservation organisations are working hard to raise awareness, conduct research and secure meaningful protection for our seagrass but any improvements will require real commitment from policy makers. Time is of the essence. It may already be too late for the spiny seahorses of Studland Bay.

The shift from seaweed or open seabed to seagrass is sudden and arresting, rather like stumbling across a clearing in a forest. Amid the usual brown and burgundy of the seaweed, the uniform emerald green is incongruent, enticing. I am fearful of damaging the seagrass or disturbing the sediment, and tread carefully around the edges of the bed. In places the tide has left the fronds dry and flattened against the seabed, while in other areas the water is knee-deep and the seagrass bed stands tall and thick as jungle grass.

I part the fronds and examine the base of each stem, hoping to find a prehensile tail curled around it, a stiff unmoving S shape, its bowed head as set as a ship's figurehead bent against the racing waves. There are two species of seahorse in the UK; both are rare and difficult to spot. I have only ever seen them in an aquarium and I know they're unlikely to be found in such a shallow seagrass bed, but nothing will stop me looking and hoping.

Tentacles of snakelocks anemones attached to the blades of seagrass dangle and sway, and a huge spider crab sidesteps away, merging into the green undergrowth. Draped along the sides of some of the leaves are clumps of red seaweed or the fragile white branches of the hydroid *Laomedea angulata*. The hydroid's tiny cups fringed with stinging tentacles give the leaves a fuzzy appearance.

I spend half an hour making a futile attempt to find a seahorse but I record dozens of other species of molluscs, worms and fish in the process. Most of this patch looks healthy, although there is some evidence of winter storm damage at one end, with some of the seagrass rhizomes exposed where the sediment has been torn away by the force of the waves.

At the far end of the meadow, where I will end my search, the seagrass is surrounded with brown kelp fronds, their tangled stipes framing the seagrass bed like tree trunks. Among them, a piece of seaweed just under half a metre long lies flat in the water. As I approach the object, it strikes me as being particularly straight and rigid. I wonder for a millisecond more before acting on instinct and plunging my hand into the water to grab it.

Immediately, a muscular tail lashes around my forearm, squeezing me with its cold grip and thrashing like a captured snake. I keep its head in the water so that it can still breathe and overcome my impulse to let go. I often see greater pipefish here and am more than familiar with their harmless but effective defensive techniques. This pipefish is smooth sided and glossy, without the hexagonal sculpture and ridges of the greater pipefish. Its golden sides are covered with regular vertical white stripes, breaking up its silhouette among the seagrass and a dark band across its face gives it a masked look. My first snake pipefish watches me with a swivelling orange eye as I admire its upturned, flared mouth, its tapering tail that it can use to hook onto pieces of seaweed just as the seahorses do, and its ability to pretend to be a piece of thong weed one minute and a twisting sea monster the next.

Snake pipefish.

My time with our largest pipefish is brief, as most marine encounters are. I keep it just long enough to confirm the species and take a couple of photos before watching it swim free. It only has two small pectoral fins and a slight fin on its back, but it loses no time in making a graceful exit into the seagrass where it blends away. I continue to watch the patch of seagrass for some time, until the water rises around my boots.

CHAPTER 22

Cup Coral

The only time I ever saw corals as a child, before I began more radical, grown-up rock pooling, was when I found the stiff branches of the sea fan, *Eunicella verrucosa*, washed up dead on the shore, usually tangled with seaweed and sometimes with a catshark egg case attached. Mostly, these sea fans were smooth and worn but occasionally the skeletons of the polyps were still attached, white and calcified as though turned to fossils. These sorry, bleached fragments are the remnants of an incredible colony, bearing little resemblance to the live animal.

Under the water, sea fans are a soft pink or white daisy chain of polyps arranged in tree-like, branching forms. Pink sea fans grow quickly at first, slowing to just a few centimetres per year as they branch, adding more polyps until they are up to a half a metre tall and at least as wide. Colonies can be long-lived; many are around 20 years old and some may live to 50. Like trees, their age is determinable through counting growth rings, but this is obviously not possible in living sea fans. These slow-branching animals live in water at least ten metres deep and are easily killed by trawling. Once pulled off the rocks of the seabed the colony cannot survive. Most importantly of all, the sea fans provide a unique habitat with several species relying on them for survival: there is a type of anemone, *Amphianthus dohrnii*, that grows only on pink sea fans; a small cowrie, *Simnia hiscocki*, which feeds exclusively on the pink sea fan; and a sea slug, *Tritonia nilsodhneri* that feeds on the polyps of this sea fan and similar species. Finding pink sea fans on the shore, while exciting, was also sad.

It did not occur to me then that I might see live corals on the shore. I assumed that the cup corals were only to be seen in books and divers' photos, but their names and colours fascinated me. It was a shock when, by accident, I came across some corals in the most familiar of places, just as though I had opened a door to a secret garden. Sometimes the places we know best are the most exotic.

It was one of so many visits to Porth Mear, the beach I spent my childhood exploring, a place where I recognised every pool, knew where the clingfish hid, where the kelp zone started, how to pick my way through hidden paths in the rocks either side of the stream. I knew how this beach shifted with the seasons and how the bursting Atlantic roared through every gap and gully so that I was always safe from surging waves. My mother, partner and son, who have also known this beach for much of their lives, were with me.

The March sun was far from strong enough to burn off any water, so we took it slowly over the slippery rocks, following the tide as it dropped to a spectacular low. I could see Mum was trying not to be adventurous, to stay safe for fear of falling on the treacherous seaweed, but she couldn't help herself and followed us ever further out into the underwater world. She turned a small rock and called out in delight. A baby spiny starfish missing one of its arms was clinging on. Next to it was a spiral of white jelly, the unmistakable eggs of a sea slug, in this case the great grey sea slug. Junior was next to shout, having found a little decorator crab, a small species of spider crab, adorned with seaweed for camouflage. Ed discovered a Cornish clingfish with pristine turquoise circles on its head, looking resplendent for the breeding season.

Looking at the scene around me, I was struck by a thought. I always assume that rock pooling is just my thing, that others around me come along just to humour me, and yet everyone was as concentrated and keen as me. A wonderful beach like this helped, but I realised in that moment that rock pooling had a unique draw. Here was an activity that a retired teacher, a child and an engineer could all enjoy equally. Perhaps there was something innately enjoyable about these unforced encounters with intriguing wildlife that went beyond my personal obsession. I had recently started my Cornish Rock Pools blog, which was far more popular than I had anticipated. This, it seemed, was why.

I clambered over the rocks to an outlying area of the beach frequently battered by breaking waves. It was difficult to access but, apart from intermittent showers of spray, all was calm. Next to me was a deep pool, beyond which, hidden behind rocks and cliffs, was the Atlantic. This was not somewhere you would want to be when a westerly gale howled in.

Huge boulders had broken away from the cliffs here many years ago and were wedged against each other, sheltering dark pools beneath their bulk. I ran my hands over their rough, barnacle-covered surface and crouched to take in the carpets of breadcrumb sponge and star ascidian sea squirts hiding underneath. An Arctic cowrie was hanging on a mucus thread under one rock and on another a sea lemon slug was lurking near its lumpy spawn. I thought I heard some choughs nearby but couldn't see them from my closed-in position beneath the cliffs. They sometimes feed on insects among the springy clifftop turf, untroubled by people in this remote corner.

I turned my head back and was drawn to a shallow pool

that dipped into a cavernous overhang that gaped like an open throat under a mighty boulder. Looking under things is what rock poolers do, so taking care not to slip into the deep water I crawled closer, dipped my head in a fruitless effort not to bang it on the rock and stared into the hole. As my eyes adjusted to the light, I saw pinpricks of brightness, like stars, orange-hued and round against the darkness.

I turned my knees painfully against the rock and stuck my head even further in, until my hair was soaked against the sodden rocky overhang. I didn't care a bit. There was no doubt in my mind. These were cup corals – star corals as they are sometimes known – arranged in constellations against the rocky sky, at the back of the overhang and at its base, under the still water of the pool.

At high tide every new wave would crash in here, booming and exploding against the dark walls, bombarding this world with overpowering force, invading and exploiting every crack and weakness in the rock. And through it all these fragile calcareous cups, bearing their bright jelly bodies and translucent glittering tentacles specked with gold, would not just cling on but thrive, taking their nutrients from the raging waters and revelling in each new blast of life-bringing power.

My mum joined me, leaning on the edge of the rock and peering round to see what I was up to. I pointed out the scarlet and gold star corals, *Balanophyllia regia*, dozens of orange and lemon dots, and attempted some photos on my camera which I passed out to her. The pictures couldn't do justice to what I was seeing but were still amazing. The intensity of the colours was like nothing we'd seen here before, even if my camera was only capable of blurred, impressionistic shots. It was as though we had found a shipwrecked galleon packed with gold ingots. We stared into the hole in disbelief. Cup corals here, on this beach we all loved, not out at sea or in a glossy book about tropical reefs.

After all my years of travelling, I had found the brightest treasures right here at home.

It was frustrating not to have a good enough camera to take sharp shots of the cup corals, and their awkward location would have made it a tight squeeze for anything larger than my simple automatic camera. Finding them would have to do for now.

I would have to wait many months for suitable tides and conditions to allow me back to this spot; on most days it's nothing more than a death trap. When I did return, I brought not just my new, better camera, but a large group of keen marine naturalists from Coastwise North Devon who joined me for a guided rock pool field trip. Despite many of them being retirees and the shore being a challenging one with slippery rocks, steep climbs, precipitous drops and the like, they bounded across the boulders undeterred and explored the shore with the intensity of a forensic investigation. Rock pooling keeps you young and fearless.

It appeared to take the group no time at all to find another huge colony under a long shelf in the rock. Water had gathered in the deep crack and among a carpet of thick sponges, coral weed and bryozoans, scores of scarlet and gold cup corals shone out. We took turns to lie on our bellies and force our cameras and heads into the narrow space, manoeuvring our necks to either side to take in the full panorama. Many of the star corals at the base of the pool were submerged enough to show their crown of tentacles; translucent cones with felty golden-yellow ridges, encircling a raised deep-orange mouth.

We sat there on those sea-gouged rocks to eat our packed lunches, swapping stories of our finds, of beaches on different parts of the coast, while breathing deeply of the salt air. Oystercatchers called across the pools and a group of walkers snaked down the cliff path opposite us, but we were too lost in

Scarlet and gold cup corals.

our world of sea life to pay attention, making the most of a rare opportunity to share and learn.

The corals were spectacular that day and we shared a sense of awe at seeing them, as well as finding a plethora of sea slugs, sea spiders, sponges and some fabulous crabs. With the help of my wonderful friends, I had learned even more about this remarkable beach, and I finally had good photos of the cup corals.

There are half a dozen cup coral species around our shores, although only two or three are likely to be found in the intertidal zone, the Devonshire cup coral, *Caryophyllia smithii*, being the one most frequently encountered by rock poolers around the south and west coasts of the UK and all around the Irish coast. It is larger than the scarlet and gold cup coral and has a slightly squashed oval outline. On rare occasions I have seen its tentacles extended, displaying their fabulous iridescent quality, framing the sculpted ridges on the inside of the cup that are banded with yellows and glowing greens.

An elegant pink, finely ridged barnacle, *Adna anglica*, grows almost exclusively on the Devonshire cup coral, often in clumps of three or four. Although it isn't considered a parasite, it may affect the coral's ability to feed. It benefits from its raised position close to the coral's tentacles; the barnacle's larvae seem to be adapted in some way to outsmart the coral's defensive stinging cells to settle on its living body.

On the shore, Devonshire cup corals are usually out of the water and retracted into their distinctive ridged cup shape. In this state, the animal lacks much of the colour and glamour it is capable of showing underwater. Like other cup corals, it prefers wave-battered holes in the rock to anything else, making it incredibly awkward to access or photograph.

Soft corals may also be encountered by the intrepid rock pooler. The wonderfully named dead man's fingers are spongey-looking white or pale orange projections that really do look horribly like water-swollen fingers. Like the sea fans, the dead man's fingers are colonies of polyps, each of which emerges as

Devonshire cup coral with *Adna anglica* barnacles. *Dr Keith Hiscock*

a cupped circle of white tentacles to feed. Like all other anemones and corals, these soft coral polyps are equipped with stinging cells, but their prey is so small that the coral's stings don't have any effect on us.

Finding a coral glowing with vibrant colour, standing proud amid the darkness of a rocky hollow, is one of those rare and humbling experiences that makes rock pooling so exciting. There is beauty in the most hostile of places.

It was tempting to keep my first coral finds as a family secret, to preserve the memory in a way that drew us together, but by sharing the knowledge with other conservationists there is better hope of monitoring and conserving them. There is also great pleasure in sharing our treasures with others who appreciate their worth. There are many things I would never have seen if others weren't prepared to share alike.

CHAPTER 23

Cephalopod

Cephalopods' strange looks have enchanted and terrified people for centuries. Unlike most other legendary beasts, the giant squid and its relatives are very much real and alive, residing in the deep oceans. The most mysterious squid of all, the colossal squid, is believed to range to at least 2.2 kilometres depth and is known mostly from the stomachs of whales and some very rare fishing catches. These are ancient animals; the very first of the cephalopods pre-date the evolution of early mammals by at least 300 million years. Ammonites and belemnites are prolific in the fossil record, but some modern cephalopods live in shallow waters and are more familiar to us, such as the octopus, squid and cuttlefish.

The closest most people come to seeing cephalopods on our shores is finding the chalky, oval cuttlefish 'bones' that are frequently deposited on the strandline. These 'bones' are the cuttlefish's internal buoyancy organ, filled with adjustable air pockets. Unlike the only other hard part of the cuttlefish's body, the beak, they are light and floaty and are therefore easily washed up on beaches, sometimes in huge numbers, because cuttlefish gather in vast schools to mate and usually die after spawning. It takes luck, patience and time, probably a lot of time, to see a live cephalopod in the rock pools, but it is possible.

The word cephalopod means 'head-foot' and the body plan of these animals is quite unlike that of other molluscs. For a start, with the exception of the six species of nautilus, they don't have an external shell. They have also developed tentacles with suckers, a fierce beak for killing their prey, and some impressive sensory organs and adaptations. Probably the most striking difference between the cephalopods and other molluscs is their swimming ability. There are some sea hares that can propel themselves through the water by flapping their parapodia, scallops can take off by quickly snapping their shells together, and the violet sea snail, *Janthina janthina*, can make a raft of bubbles and drift over huge distances on the ocean's surface, but none of these molluscs comes close to having the swimming ability of cephalopods. With perfect control over their buoyancy, cuttlefish, squid and octopuses (or octopodes, if you prefer) can hover in the water, change speed and direction, and dart in to strike prey in the blink of an eye. It is hard to believe that these resourceful, intelligent and speedy animals have anything in common with garden snails or slugs, but strange things most certainly do happen at sea.

My own fascination with them began with their eyes. The cuttlefish, like all cephalopods, has highly evolved eyes which work in a very similar way to those of vertebrates. The similarity, however, is largely coincidental: a product of convergent evolution. The last common ancestor we shared was probably around 500 million years or more ago and might have been a simple marine animal like a worm or leech. This creature would have had light-sensitive eyes, probably simple photoreceptors. As cephalopods and vertebrates evolved, their eyes became ever more complex and sensitive to help them to catch prey or avoid predators. In this way, they independently developed similar solutions, but with subtle differences. Stare into the eyes of a cuttlefish and you will see that they are quite alien to us.

The common cuttlefish's eye has a black pupil, which moves and changes size to let in light in a similar way to our own. The pupil, however, is only round in complete darkness – otherwise it has a wavy W shape. Although the exact benefits of this shape are not fully understood, it is thought to help improve the perception of contrasting variable light conditions. This could be of great benefit to the cuttlefish in shallow seas where sunlight streams from above, while the conditions below are darker. The cuttlefish's ability to equalise the image and see the areas of low light with greater clarity is an important advantage for a predator.

A mystery that has long intrigued scientists studying cephalopods is that, although these animals do not have colour receptor cones in their retina as we do, they still manage to change their colour to match their surroundings. Berkeley and

The distinctive W-shaped pupil of the common cuttlefish (photo taken in an aquarium).

Harvard researchers think that the wavy pupil may mean that cephalopods are not colour-blind, although they are unlikely to perceive colour quite as we do. Humans with dilated pupils can sometimes perceive a halo of colour around objects, a phenomenon known as a chromatic aberration which occurs when the transparent lens of our eye acts as a prism, separating out the colours in the white light. It seems that the special shape of the cephalopod's pupil has a widening effect, allowing light to enter the animal's eyes from multiple angles at once, accentuating the chromatic aberration. By altering the depth of its eyeball, the cephalopod seems to be able to focus the different colour patterns of these aberrations, using relative focus to deduce the colours.

Research has also shown that the skins of the cuttlefish, squid and octopus are as remarkable as their eyes due to the presence of light-sensitive molecules called opsins. In the cuttlefish and squid, opsins are found within the chromatophores. These little sacs of pigment relax and contract to change the colour of the cuttlefish's skin. In the octopus the opsins are found in hair-like cilia on the skin. It seems that these opsins allow the cephalopods' skin to perceive light and perhaps even colours. In tests, octopus skin has been shown to be able to adjust its pigmentation in response to changing light without any messages having to pass through the brain. In cuttlefish and squid, the function of the opsin molecules is less clear. The potential human applications of automatically changing camouflaging materials has not escaped the attention of scientists, especially those looking to develop invisibility devices for military and other applications.

I first met a cuttlefish on a dive under Swanage Pier. I still have no idea how I kept my regulator in my mouth as it fell open in delight and awe. With a rippling mantle and changing colours the cuttlefish swam straight towards my face. I was thrilled as it approached, two of its eight arms raised above its head, like the Karate Kid about to do the crane move. This was a discerning animal that was showing it was not going to be intimidated by a pair of bubble-blowing neoprene wearers staring at it. My buddy and I backed off respectfully, which is always best, and watched from the corner of our eyes as the triumphant cuttlefish nonchalantly drifted away to patrol the seabed, or perhaps to find more divers to intimidate.

The tentacle-lifting trick was not a friendly wave but a threat to attack. Some people, on encountering a cuttlefish, make the mistake of putting their hands out to touch or coax the animal, often making the painful discovery that cuttlefish can easily bite through dive gloves. Their razor-sharp beak is, after all, mostly used to crack through the shells of crabs and molluscs, so human skin is no challenge. As if that wasn't enough in itself, all cuttlefish and octopuses and some squid also have a venomous bite, which they use to stun their prey. Their venom might not have much effect on humans but I wasn't prepared to use my face to find out. More than with any other marine animal I have ever met, it felt as though the cuttlefish, not the humans, was in charge of that meeting.

Given the numerous accounts of how octopuses in aquaria squirt water to short-circuit annoying light bulbs, solve puzzles to access their food and show the ability to recognise different people, even if those people are wearing the same uniform, there is no doubt that cephalopods can be smart. Octopuses are also known to spring open the lids of their tanks, pop into a neighbouring tank to feast on the occupants before heading back to their own tank as if nothing had happened, as well as using their lack of a skeleton to squeeze through any hole that is larger than their mouth (their only solid part) to escape or hide. One species of octopus has also been observed using tools to build shelters.

I assumed that diving or visiting the aquarium would be the only ways to encounter live cephalopods, and for the most part I was right. In several decades of exploring the shore, I have met a couple of cephalopod species but, as yet, no common cuttlefish. However, the tales of other rock poolers suggest that it is perfectly possible and nothing will stop me looking.

One wonderful story was related to me by a friend and her daughter, who were on a beach beside the chalk cliffs of South East England during a big low tide. They were taken aback to find courting cuttlefish couples putting on their full mating display in the open shallows. The male cuttlefish had transformed their bodies into bold zebra stripes with a fringe of white spots against the black of their frilled mantle. Their faces were maroon, as though literally on heat. After showing off for a while, the dominant male turned head-to-head with the female, grabbing her by the face with his sucker arms. This is when he will have passed her a special gift: his sperm packet. For this, he uses an arm that is adapted for the purpose.

As the tide came in, my friends left the scene behind, with the male still guarding his female, waiting for her to envelop her eggs in black ink and lay them. The whole process may take many hours.

Occasionally these eggs, known as sea grapes, become detached from the seaweed or seagrass on which they are laid and wash up on the tideline. One of the reasons I often take a bucket to the beach is in the hope of finding unhatched cuttlefish or squid eggs. I keep an unused tank at home for any such emergency. With the right care, these stranded eggs can be kept cool and oxygenated until they hatch: something I would love to do, even if I wouldn't be able to sleep for fear of missing the big event. When they are born, the cuttlefish are already perfectly formed and able to change colour and squirt ink. Hatchlings can be raised in captivity for a short time if suitable food is available, ensuring they become large and strong enough to stand a good chance of survival, but they may become aggressive towards one another as they grow. A friend describes the three-week-old cuttlefish hatchlings he reared from some rescued eggs, 'turning black with rage, locked in face-to-face combat'. He hastened to return them to the wild before they started to do each other serious harm.

Every year some friends from Essex visit us. They love Cornwall for the fish and chips, the scenery, the gift shops and the scones. They are not what you might call 'outdoorsy' people. I have a suspicion they may not even own a pair of wellies, yet every year without fail they come rock pooling with me. Not only do they come willingly, they say they look forward to it all year.

Increasingly, they have taken to planning their holidays around the tide times, to make sure we can fit at least one rock pooling session into their break. There's a lot of slipping and splashing, squeals of excitement or of fear, a huge number of 'Oh my God's and above all a lot of fun. Over the years we have held squat lobsters and starfish, looked at variegated scallops and blennies, and disagreed often over whether the worms and slugs are amazing or plain disgusting. (I will have to keep working on them.)

My favourite session of all was the one where we almost saw another species of cephalopod, the little cuttlefish. In a deep pool, knee-high in non-native sargassum weed, I parted the tangled strands with my fingertips, trying to mimic a gentle current to reveal any animals that might be growing or swimming there. A couple of prawns hovered in the shelter of the clump, while a hermit crab took a short stroll across the sand below before swivelling its shell back over its head. My friends were already looking at a hermit crab wearing a turban top shell and were taking photos, so I left this one where it was.

I took a step to the right, to the next part of the seaweed forest, and brushed it with my knee by accident. In a shimmering flash a whole group of animals shot out; prawns I thought because they were swimming in a backwards motion, their dark eyes pointing towards me as they swam away. They were more lozenge shaped than prawns, about the size of cough sweets. Within a fraction of a second, I realised that their movement wasn't right for prawns either. They seemed to glide more smoothly, hold themselves differently, and those eyes ... It was hard to see much detail without getting closer, but the edges of their eyes gleamed with gold and the pupils were strange, nothing like the compound prawn eyes or fish eyes. I was sure they were cuttlefish, but with no net, my nearest bucket lying on the rocks on the far side of the pool, and knowing just how quickly these creatures could camouflage themselves, there was no point in doing anything except watch. I called out to my friends but there was already nothing to see. It was a huge pool and the tiny cuttlefish swooped away towards an overhang, already almost invisible as their camouflage kicked in, and they would be burying themselves up to the eyes under the sand in seconds. Given that these animals can camouflage themselves not just against their background but taking account of the perspective of any potential predator, it would be a hopeless search, so I had to admit defeat.

As I drew my eyes away from the spot where I had seen the cephalopods no one would believe in, I saw something new in the water. Three or four dark pea-sized splodges were suspended there, the water around them grey and cloudy. I gave a triumphant shout, scooped one of these black splodges into a tub and rushed to show my bemused friends. Startled by my knee or foot, the little creatures had squirted ink and mucus into the water, something all the cephalopods do to secure an escape. It was a poor substitute for showing my friends the actual animals and they were rightly unconvinced, but I was ecstatic. This was my first brush in the rock pools with cephalopods, the creatures of the deep, creatures of legend and marvel. They were almost definitely the species called the little cuttlefish, *Sepiola atlantica*, which is actually a bobtail squid, not a cuttlefish. They don't grow much bigger than the ones I saw that day and are the most likely species to turn up in shallow, sandy pools where they are almost impossible to see. Luck, timing and patience are everything.

The mollusc identification course I presented for the Coastal Creatures project in North Devon was always going to be a hands-on session. I arrived armed with a colourful slideshow packed with identification tips that work in the field and armfuls of jars of labelled gastropod and bivalve shell specimens: finally that shell collection in my parents' spare bedroom had been put to good use.

When I first moved back to the coast eight years ago, I struggled to tell the top shell species apart, but now I can recognise them and many other species of mollusc at a glance. Despite this, some scientific keys will always bring me out in a sweat. Being self-taught, I've never heard most of the scientific names pronounced anywhere except in my own head, but no one seems to mind and most of the people I work with seem as bewildered as I am by the constant changes in species names. I am only too aware that it is impossible for any of us to know everything about our diverse marine wildlife and sharing is what these courses are all about.

Accessibility is the wonderful thing about naturalism: anyone who is willing and able to look can make discoveries; even in the least likely environments, there is always something to see. I remember being told when I first began submitting my sightings to my local records centre, after I moved back to Cornwall, that even with my limited knowledge at that time I was making a valuable contribution. So few people send in their records that we know little about the distribution of even the more common species. I have often been the very first person to ever submit a record of a limpet from a beach. There are huge holes in our knowledge that anyone can help to fill. Sharing what we know and working together at group events like my molluscs course always pays dividends. They are gold mines for my own learning, even though I'm the teacher.

At this particular event, I was going to see my first octopus.

'We probably won't see any cephalopods,' I admitted to the group before our field trip to Lee Bay, but I still showed some identification slides and requested that anyone finding a cuttlefish or octopus should shout at the top of their lungs. There was reason to hope we might find something, following several sightings of curled octopus around UK shores over the previous months, including one found tantalisingly close to this beach. I may have offered special prizes from the biscuit selection. I continued to remind the group of this as I pulled my waders on and as we walked to the beach. I mentioned it again on arrival, just in case they hadn't realised how serious I was. Although experience told me that cephalopods were few and far between in the intertidal zone, it also told me that when a large group of keen, eager-eyed rock poolers are exploring a place, the chances of finding interesting things increases exponentially.

My main focus was on finding sea slugs; never an easy task on an unfamiliar beach and under time pressure. I was at the end of a narrow rocky gully, scanning a piece of sponge for signs of sea slugs when a shout went up from the other side of the beach, below the cliffs. Before the third syllable of 'Octopus!' entered my ears I was off, running full pelt towards the cry. Wearing waders while sprinting through knee-deep water, through sinking sand and over rocks, is no mean feat. As I sloshed and flailed across the shore, shouting to others to follow, it occurred to me that this was probably a joke that the group had decided to play on me. I'm not usually given to paranoia but I had laid on my desperation to find an octopus a bit thick and someone could so easily make a few quid these days by filming a crazed woman in waders trying to run through deep water and, in all likelihood, falling flat on my face any second now.

Regardless of my suspicions, I kept running, and next time I looked up from my stumbling I could see a crowd gathering around one of our participants, local naturalist Rob Durrant, who had raised the shout. I knew him to be extremely capable of finding strange things, so I forgot all my doubts. I joined the group and saw he was holding a transparent collecting pot the size of a small tumbler aloft for us all to see. Crammed inside, amid a jumble of arms, was a miniature but unmistakeable octopus. Its long, tapering limbs swirled and probed the inside of the container, curling and unfurling like a psychedelic spinning pattern, while it watched us through elongated black pupils.

Before our eyes it transformed from near-white to a terracotta red, from bumpy to smooth, the chromatophores hard at work in its skin, contracting and relaxing to alter the visible pigment in bursts and waves, constantly adjusting, to the joy of the surrounding mollusc-watchers.

Along each of its eight arms a single line of powerful suckers rippled, gripping at the Perspex, probing and tasting it. There are only two species of octopus in UK waters: this one was a curled octopus, *Eledone cirrhosa*. The other species, the common octopus, *Octopus vulgaris*, has two lines of suckers on each arm and grows larger. In our excitement we forgot to look at the octopus's third arm to see if it lacked suckers on the tip. If it did,

Curled octopus, *Eledone cirrhosa. Rob Durrant*

it would be a male, because this arm is specially adapted for mating. The curled octopus tends to be rather coy about showing its arm-tips in any case, rolling up the ends of its arms into tight spirals, as this one did, giving them the appearance of tendrils on a climbing plant. Despite their reputation as escape artists, this one didn't seem in a hurry to jump out of the open pot and even sat reasonably quietly on Rob's hand for a photo. As soon as it was released back to its pool, however, it shot off. Whether it squeezed back beneath the large flat slab of stone under which it was found or changed its appearance to disappear from sight, it was lost in a second.

CHAPTER 24

Jellyfish

Jellyfish swarms are a regular but entirely unpredictable feature of shore life. For months there will be none at all, then from nowhere, most often in the summer or autumn, the sea and the pools become a tangle of gracefully pumping bells that tumble in the waves until the tideline piles up with their spent bodies. This is a natural part of their lifecycle and as one generation dies on a beach, another will be developing, first as planula larvae in the plankton, then as polyps attached to the substrate, which release tiny ephyra that swim freely. Only as adults do they develop into the jellyfish that send swimmers into a panic each year.

In their jellyfish form they can travel huge distances, whether actively swimming or being carried by currents, tidal flows and winds. Even though our largest species, the lion's mane jellyfish, can be up to two metres in diameter, jellyfish are considered part of the plankton drifting the open oceans. Brainless, eyeless, the only input they have about their world comes from rudimentary sensory nerves in the base of their tentacles which can detect light and smells. These wanderers of the oceans are found all around the globe, in shallow seas and in the deepest oceans. Despite their simplicity these invertebrates have been around for at least 500 million years and probably longer, surviving multiple extinction events. They have no bones, but their imprints in soft sediment have been found in the fossil record.

When numbers of predatory fish and other species decline due to overfishing, changes in climate, or an increase in the acidity of the ocean due to increased carbon dioxide absorption, jellyfish and their relatives tend to thrive. They increase in numbers until they swarm, with impacts on the ecosystem balance. Jellyfish population explosions can also cause other issues when they lodge in the nets at fish farms and either starve the fish of oxygen or sting them, causing the death of fish either directly through their toxins or indirectly by creating lesions that become infected. Jellyfish can also clog the water intakes at nuclear power stations.

Sometimes just one species washes in, but more often there is a colourful mixture of different jellyfish that collects in our tidal gullies as a soup of jumbled bells and tentacles. Identification of species at the adult stage is easy based on their striking colours: the compass jellyfish is adorned with dark brown V markings like the points of a compass; the mauve stinger is covered with purple bumpy spots rather like the flecks of a strawberry and packs a strong sting for its size; the vast but harmless barrel jellyfish is unmistakeably huge, rubbery and opaque, with just a thin band of purple around its chunky sides; the lion's mane jellyfish has a yellow fuzz of enormously long trailing tentacles; and the blue jellyfish is, of course, usually blue but can sometimes be brown. The most common jellyfish of all, the moon jellyfish, is transparent with four pink or purple incomplete circles in the middle, somewhat like a cucumber slice.

At family events children scoop jellyfish into buckets to watch their strange pulsing movements. Despite their fearsome, trailing tentacles, most European species only have weak stings

– no worse than stinging nettles – and some don't harm humans at all, although the lion's mane jellyfish can pack a punch and they are all best left alone. Many people still believe the myth that you should wee on jellyfish stings to treat them. I hate to spoil anyone's fun, but there's no truth in it. Vinegar or similar acidic anti-sting preparations can help, ideally followed by immersion in hot water, which must be 45 degrees Celsius or above. Given that human urine is not going to be any warmer than body temperature (around 37 degrees Celsius), it is thankfully useless. I know from first-hand experience that it's not a great idea to swim face first into trailing tentacles or to wade into pools full of jellyfish, but even without vinegar or hot water (and most definitely without any urine) the effects have been mild and short-lived.

Like all the other life forms we've met, jellyfish are part of a wider ecosystem and food chain in which they are both predators and prey. They are fairly undiscerning in their own diet, eating almost anything that comes into contact with the paralysing sting of the nematocysts on their tentacles, from tiny planktonic animals to young fish. Some young fish specialise in sheltering from larger fish under the protection of jellyfish tentacles, somehow avoiding being stung themselves.

Leatherback turtles, on the other hand, eat almost only one thing: jellyfish. Travelling up to 10,000 miles per year, these two-metre-long giants follow the jellyfish blooms on ocean currents. Some are known from tracking projects to cross the entire Pacific Ocean, from Japan to the west coast of the USA, gobbling jellyfish as they go, using the spines that line their oesophagus to impale and trap their slippery prey to stop them slipping back out of their mouths.

It is unfortunately almost impossible for a hungry leatherback turtle to distinguish between a swirling, translucent jellyfish and a swirling, translucent plastic bag. Those spines in its oesophagus make it especially hard for the turtle to prevent the choking plastic from sticking in its gullet. Almost all turtles that have been examined worldwide are now found to have plastic in their stomachs. Entanglement and suffocation in nets and injuries from contact with boat propellers are also deadly risks to the turtles, which must surface regularly to breathe. When turtles are found on our shores, they are either dead or are stranded and in imminent danger. Few will make it, but some, like Myrtle the loggerhead turtle, stranded in North Uist in the Western Isles in 2004, are successfully nursed back to health. She was flown to the Canary Isles to be released back into warmer, richer waters where her chances of survival were higher.

Another far less well-known visitor that arrives with the jellyfish bloom is a little parasitic amphipod, *Hyperia galba*, which specialises in hiding away on and in the body of various jellyfish. At risk of looking slightly demented, I regularly kneel in the sand to examine the bodies of washed-up jellyfish for this little sandhopper stowaway. It is often lodged under the bell and seems to be especially fond of taking up residence in the jellyfish's gonads. It's easily spotted through the transparent jelly as it gazes out through oversized compound green eyes that glow in the light. These tiny creatures only live on jellyfish and throw their lot in with them, sailing the seas under their protection, travelling huge distances, but unable to escape the fate of their host when the jellyfish washes ashore or is eaten, perishing alongside it.

Confusingly to anyone new to studying marine life, jellyfish are just one class of animals within a much larger phylum, the cnidarians, in which all the animals are linked by having stinging cells. Some other members of the phylum, such as the anemones and corals, are easily distinguished from the 'true jellyfish' or

Scyphozoa. However, lots of other free-swimming cnidarians look very much like jellyfish and, just like the jellyfish, will occasionally drift into the intertidal zone to the delight of rock poolers and beach combers. The hydroid *Velella velella*, known as the by-the-wind sailor, can wash inshore in such enormous numbers that it sometimes carpets beaches with small discs of the deepest indigo fringed with short tentacles. It floats on, rather than in, the water, its thin sail set diagonally across its body catching the prevailing wind, propelling it vast distances across the sea, often together with thousands of others that have their sails in the same orientation. By-the-wind sailors with their sail set on the opposite diagonal will also raft together, spreading the species' chances of success. Sometimes violet sea snails wash up alongside them. Rather like a garden snail in size and shape, these striking purple or blue shells build rafts of bubbles around their operculum and use this float to allow them to sail alongside the *Velella velella*, on which they feed. They are also partial to eating the Portuguese man o'war.

I have been heartened in recent years by the number of members of the public who have contacted me with concerns about the appearance of thousands of pieces of cellophane on the beaches, showing a huge surge in the level of awareness about plastic pollution in our seas. While marine plastic is an enormous problem, many of these cellophane reports turn out to be due to a mass stranding of *Velella velella* hydroids. After just a few days on the shore, the by-the-wind sailors lose their blue pigment and dry out, becoming transparent, light and only faintly ridged, just like light, clear plastic.

It has taken me decades to see some other stars of the free-swimming cnidarian world. Siphonophores are a particularly bizarre group of colonial animals that often take the form of a gelatinous swimming tube but are hugely variable in colour, structure and habits. Although individual members of the colony may be only a few millimetres long, they can come together to form large animals, with one deep water species, *Praya dubia*, measuring up to 50 metres, making it one of the world's longest creatures. Although they are only rarely to be found in the rock pools, they are present in many shallow seas, and a mass invasion of the siphonophore *Apolemia uvaria* was credited with causing the deaths of many farmed salmon in Norway in 1997. The long string of zooids works together like a swimming strand of pinkish seaweed to catch and digest their prey.

When a species of siphonophore that sometimes washes into our coasts made a mass appearance in autumn 2017, I wanted to rush to the beach to look for them. My family were less enthusiastic about spending a cold, windy October morning on a beach looking for animals with a ferocious sting. My son, who has something of a specialism in animals, plants and mushrooms that can kill or seriously injure you, was particularly insistent that he would no way go within a mile of a Portuguese man o'war, but promises of hot chocolate afterwards had him pulling on his wellies.

The beach was bleak and empty when we arrived, apart from a few people walking their dogs along a distant path, their heads bowed against the wind. We crunched away across the gravelly sand, over the kelp-strewn tideline to the rocks beyond. None of us had ever seen a Portuguese man o'war before, but it took less than a minute to find one that had been blown against the rocks near the top of the shore, its bright blue tentacles coiled in a soggy heap in a narrow pool. For all his reluctance to venture onto a beach with these creatures, my son was drawn near in open-mouthed wonder.

'It's like a rainbow pasty,' he breathed, maintaining a respectful distance.

The float was a puffy oval with distinct crimping along one edge. It was impossible to pin down its colours which were all shades of glimmering pink, blue and purple, constantly changing in the feeble sunlight. Unlike most British wildlife which turns out to be smaller than you expect, as anyone who has ever seen a real puffin or kingfisher will testify, these strange siphonophores were larger than I expected. Some were medium pasty size but others were easily larger.

To my son's horror I grabbed a pair of rubber gloves out of my bag and scooped one of the colourful pasties into a bucket of seawater. I've seen other people pick them up by the gas-filled float with their bare hands, but I didn't trust myself not to accidentally brush the tentacles. We stared through the bucket's transparent sides at the bundle of blue beneath the float which was unfurling and pulsing in strange ways.

This siphonophore would have started with a single fertilised egg, which split into various separate animals, the zooids, each cloning itself over and again to produce the recognisable colony,

A stranded Portuguese man o'war.

living together under a single float. There are individual zooids that are entirely focused on digestion, or capturing prey, or on reproduction. All are reliant on life in the colony for survival. Each colony is either male or female and these animals probably reproduce by broadcasting eggs and sperm into the water.

As we watched, the stinging tentacles unfurled, showing their distinctive structure of minute discs piled on top of each other. These tentacles are able to curl and retract completely under the float, but when feeding they trail at least ten metres deep as a deadly sweeping curtain of stinging cells.

As expected, the shore was littered with Portuguese man o'war, which decorated many of the pools and gullies with their iridescent colours. Among them were a few by-the-wind sailors, also carried in on the blustery winds.

Before we headed home for the promised hot chocolate, we released a Portuguese man o'war into one end of a wide pool to watch how speedily it was picked up by the wind and carried to the other side. In seconds it had flipped itself upright, with its crimped sail pointing skywards, its tentacles lengthening behind it as it drifted, then beached on the far rocks.

Back in a nearby inlet some months later, when the warm air and long days had returned, I witnessed a jelly invasion of another kind that I had long hoped to see: a huge bloom of comb jellies. These transparent jellies are in a different phylum from the jellyfish, hydroids, siphonophores and anemones. They are not cnidarians because they do not use stinging tentacles to capture their prey. Instead they are armed with colloblasts, which fire out sticky substances to entangle and trap their food. However, you would know none of this by looking at them.

Looking at them is not, in fact, as easy as it sounds. I had spent around 20 minutes knee-deep in water, looking at a minute *Doto* sea slug grazing on the thick fringe of hydroids growing all over the bladderwrack before something grabbed my attention. At the edge of my vision something caught the light; perhaps a fish I thought. I fixed the spot and watched for a few seconds but saw nothing.

Another flash further off to the right confirmed I hadn't entirely lost the plot. I tried to scoop the creature producing the lights into my hands, but it was so transparent I kept losing sight of it. Even when it was in my hands I couldn't feel it there and it kept slipping out. I knew it must be a comb jelly, but this was larger than the small comb jellies known as sea gooseberries that I'd seen just a couple of times on the tideline. Unlike those, it was also very much alive and swimming away from me at a surprising speed. The strange rainbow lights pulsing in lines down its body were coming from its cilia; lines of tiny hair-like paddles that were working together to row the comb jelly through the water, scattering the light and producing a sparkling light show.

Every time the cilia moved out of the light or stopped beating, the jelly seemed to disappear. It was so transparent that I could see every detail of the seaweed beneath it and my camera refused to accept that it was there at all, focusing on everything but the jelly. Instead of being spherical like a sea gooseberry, this comb jelly was an elongated hollow sack shape, with a slight pink tinge, a *Beroe cucumis*. When it slipped away through a gap in a rock, I stood back and looked around me more carefully. It took a minute or two, but gradually my eyes focused into the water and I spotted another, and another. With a growing sense of incredulity, I realised that the water around me was teeming with comb jellies, some only small but others bigger than my hand, all of them pulsating in rainbow colours, doing their disappearing and reappearing tricks.

Among the larger *Beroe cucumis*, I came across some smaller sea gooseberries, their two feathery tentacles trailing beneath them as they flashed like Christmas lights.

Another tiny jelly passed my left leg: a transparent circle of jelly with a purple cross marked in its middle and a dotted pattern around its circumference. It swam like a jellyfish, contracting its bell vigorously as though it were in a hurry to get somewhere. This was yet another category of jelly: the free-swimming medusa stage of *Clytia hemisphaerica*, a hydroid that usually lives attached to rocks or seaweed, similar to the ones that my *Doto* slug had been feeding on earlier. These transparent jellies are so easily overlooked that they are not often recorded but are fascinating, so unlike their adult forms that it is hard to believe they are the same creature.

As the tide began to creep up my legs, the comb jellies seemed to thin out, perhaps moving on to somewhere else to feed. I carried on taking my blurry photos of them and watching their colours until the water reached my waist, then reluctantly stepped back. I returned to that inlet several times over the next week and never saw another one.

Unlike the animals of the upper and midshore, jellyfish and their other pelagic relatives like the comb jellies are only visitors to the intertidal zone and are not adapted to the extremes of this environment. Many are dead or dying by the time they come ashore, having been churned through the waves and against rocks, and once they are deposited on the beach they dehydrate rapidly, until eventually they shrivel and disappear. Some of their close relatives like the hydroids, however, are permanent residents of the lower shore and shallow seas.

When the UK government decided to move ahead with creating Marine Conservation Zones around the coast of England, they tasked DEFRA, working with Natural England and others, to devise criteria that such areas should meet. DEFRA duly came up with lists of habitats and species which were considered to be in need of particular protection or were indicators of diverse or vulnerable ecosystems. Two of the species on the list were stalked jellyfish.

Despite their presence in various marine wildlife identification books, it is fair to say that, prior to the Marine Conservation Zone designation process, very few of the people recording wildlife on our shores had ever seen a stalked jellyfish. With the prize of achieving protection for important local habitats within our grasp, I was one of many local naturalists around the country who grabbed a list of the designated 'Species of Conservation Importance' and treated it like a bingo card on beaches which fell within the proposed zones.

Naturalists are a determined and sometimes competitive bunch and now, with the aid of social media, we're able to find out about any interesting finds faster than ever before – grabbing our wellies and rushing out to try our luck on our own local patches. We have come a long way from the era of the whiskered or bonnet-wearing Victorian collectors, some of whom had no qualms about decimating populations through their need to add to their specimen collection. Although beards are all the rage again, naturalists these days mostly collect photos and the aim of our work is to understand, restore and increase populations. From the cities to the remotest parts of the coast and countryside, our small army of largely unpaid and often self-taught specialists are quick to mobilise, and unwavering in our commitment to force the hand of decision-makers into giving the best possible deal to wildlife. If there were any stalked jellyfish out there, we were prepared to stand in those windswept pools, wild-haired and red-eyed, staring into the water until they were found.

Looking for a creature that is generally no more than two centimetres long and is perfectly camouflaged to blend in with seaweed, on a shore a mile wide that is thick with tangled seaweed, is far more demanding than looking for a needle in a haystack, but I was never one to let logic get in the way of a project. I spent many, many hours looking without quite knowing what I was looking for, given that I had never seen one of these fabled creatures and photos of them were sparse. The black and white drawings in my Hayward and Ryland book didn't give much away and even the colour illustrations in the Collins weren't much to go on, bearing little resemblance to the real thing, possibly because they were drawn from descriptions or dead specimens, rather than live animals or photos.

My lucky break came when a stalked jellyfish jumped out at me. Not literally, as they live attached by a stalk to algae and, other than occasionally letting go and flinging themselves into the current in search of a new home, or a slow, looping caterpillar-style relocation along the seaweed, they stay fixed in one place. What I found was a *Calvadosia cruxmelitensis* stalked jelly, often known as the Maltese Cross jelly due to the cross-like pattern of white nematocysts that trace the outline of its eight tentacle-bearing arms. This stalked jelly is brilliantly camouflaged among the red seaweeds on which it lives, with a deep maroon background colour. Like several other species of stalked jelly, it especially favours dense fringes of a branching reddish seaweed called *Chondrus crispus*, also known as Irish moss or carrageen, that grow around some lower shore rocks, and the bushy red seaweeds that grow as epiphytes on the carrageen. Pretty much all UK species of seaweed are edible, but carrageen is harvested for a substance known as carrageenan, which is used as a thickener in ice creams and other food products.

The stalked jelly I found, however, had taken up residence on some bright green sea lettuce in a very shallow pool, making it stand out beautifully.

I may even have shouted, 'Bingo!'

Occasionally double-headed stalked jellyfish occur, like this *Calvadosia cruxmelitensis*.

Since my first encounter, I have recorded hundreds of stalked jellies of four different species in my local area and further afield, and have even taught others how to find and identify them. The good news is that this evidence contributed to the creation of the Whitsand and Looe Bay Marine Conservation Zone in 2013. A further round of designations followed in 2016, and some similar protected areas have been created or are proposed around the Welsh, Northern Irish and Scottish coasts. So far, however, there are very few fishing no-take zones.

The diverse seaweed communities in areas where stalked jellyfish are found provide a rich habitat for a plethora of species of invertebrates and fish. These habitats merit protection for their own sake and ensuring they are conserved has the added benefit of helping to protect and replenish fish stocks. But creating protected areas is only effective if it comes with public information, education, research and enforcement. Otherwise all we have are paper parks. Marine wildlife has no respect for borders and no part of our coast exists in isolation, so policies are also needed to ensure that the whole marine environment is protected and managed. Without this, there will be adverse effects for the unprotected areas. It remains to be seen whether and how the Marine Conservation Zone designations will achieve the goal of creating an effective series of protected areas, but they can only represent a first step in addressing the wider challenges of marine conservation.

Focusing on tiny things in the rock pools for so long does strange things to my eyes, a bit like staring at a bright light for too long. After a few hours I see things that aren't there, and if I close my eyes I can still see whatever I've spent my day looking at.

It can make for strange dreams. More than once I have awoken convinced that I have found something amazing. The disappointment of discovering that the wonderful pool I was just watching was only in my head is tempered by knowing that there is still a chance of going out into the real world and seeing the comb jellies, seahorses, slugs and rays of my dreams. There is so much I still haven't seen, so much still to be learned about even the commonest of rock pool creatures. Sometimes I find a curious-looking stalked jellyfish in my dreams among a kaleidoscope of standard species, and my intense puzzling wakes me. Perhaps there are new species of these little-studied animals out there. Much as I would love to be the person who finds them, I am glad it is not as easy as it seems in my idealised dreams. Where would the reward be if discovery were that simple?

Feeding the Addiction

Patauger jour et nuit par n'importe quel temps même où l'on sait ne rien trouver, de l'eau au nombril ou aux chevilles, fouiller partout, algue ou pieuvre, s'hypnotiser sur une mare sinistre où tout vous guette alors que rien n'y vit — extase de n'importe quel intoxiqué ...

Wading around in water up to your ankles or navel, day or night, in all kinds of weather, even when there is no hope of finding anything; investigating everything whether it is algae or octopus; being hypnotised by a sinister pond where everything seems to be watching you even when nothing lives there. This is the ecstasy of an addict ...

Jean Painlevé, *Les Pieds dans l'Eau*, 1935

There has never been a moment in my life when I haven't been drawn to the sea. Addictions are usually driven by a desire to avoid fear, but rock pooling is an addiction like no other. The unknown is what pulls me in, what drives me to stand at the edge of the raging sea in all weathers, to stare into those deep still pools and force myself closer to whatever may lurk there. Even the most familiar inhabitants of the shore, the barnacles, limpets and sandhoppers, have lives that are so alien and incredible to us that we cannot ever fully know them. As I take each step further out, into a world that is not mine, at the edge of the vast ocean, I lose myself, and know more fully than at any other time that I am the merest speck in the world. I have no special place, and yet I am present and part of it, alongside all of these breathtaking life forms. It is at once terrifying and relaxing.

My addiction draws me ever deeper, towards bioluminescent glowing tides of plankton; sponges that contain toxins that inhibit the growth of cancer cells; fish that build nests; delicate sea spiders that live among the seaweed; pseudoscorpions and other air-breathing mites and insects that hide in air pockets in the rocks; sea cucumbers that can spit out sticky white threads to deter predators; and sun stars, feather stars, crabs with claws five times the length of their bodies and the possibility of discovering something that no one has seen before.

To stand alongside a fully-grown shark, amid a light-show of flashing comb jellies, under an overhang packed with corals or by a pool of fighting hermit crabs, must surely be up there with the most incredible wildlife experiences any person can have. Coming this close to wild creatures is a humbling reminder of the responsibilities that come with being a human. It makes me think more about treading lightly, both literally on the shore, but also more widely in my choices that impact on the world around me.

In the modern world, where three-quarters of our children spend less time outside than is granted to prisoners, and where the strain on the natural world to support our levels of consumption is increasing all the time, the need for connecting with nature has never been greater. Every child should have the chance to hold a pretty shell, watch crabs run sideways and experience the wonder of the rock pools. Every adult should rediscover the shore too. There is every likelihood that it will become a habit; lead people to discover more, question more and care more. So be it.

If rock pooling is a 'fix', then I, like Painlevé and all those marine wildlife obsessives that have gone before me, am a confirmed and willing addict.

Although conservationists have always worked together to share information and concerns, the level of mobilisation that emerged to support the designation of Marine Protected Areas and to gather the required evidence felt like something very new. The 'Blue Planet effect' has also been immense and timely, generating a buzz of enthusiasm for marine wildlife and for tackling issues like plastic pollution and climate change that threaten the balance and well-being of our marine ecosystem. For all its faults, social media is not only making networking between marine specialists and enthusiasts easier, it is also enabling far more people to experience the beauty and mystery of the marine world and to understand the threats to it.

With this growth in awareness and activism, there has never been a better time to get involved with marine conservation and science. Vibrant and welcoming marine and beach cleaning groups are springing up all around the country and are looking for new members. You no longer need prior knowledge to contribute to new discoveries, with opportunities to take part in citizen science and education projects through organisations like the Marine Conservation Society, the Shark Trust, the Marine Biological Association and the Porcupine Marine Natural History Society. There are also many exciting marine biology and conservation programmes available at universities and colleges for those who do want to take it further. The Wildlife Trusts' Shoresearch Project, which has been so enormously successful in my own local area in bringing together local experts and members of the public to record rock pool wildlife and monitor the arrival of alien species, is now being rolled out nationally and will bring the wonders of the rock pools to more people than ever before.

Ask any naturalist how their passion for wildlife developed and they will usually tell stories of jam jars full of tadpoles, of turning over logs to discover insects or of stalking the rock pools with a bucket or net. Experiencing wildlife for yourself is how the obsession begins and it is never too late to start learning. There is also a growing wealth of marine education programmes reaching out to youngsters in schools, through youth groups and societies and through the events that local organisations are running, which is proving effective in recruiting the next generation of naturalists.

Whether you prefer to browse some of the attractive new photographic field guides and the ever-expanding range of online information, watch a film about marine conservation, or pull your wellies on and head for the shore, it is easier than ever to discover rock pool wildlife.

Conserving our diverse and fragile marine ecosystems will mean some big, creative thinking in future, but we are best at finding ways to tackle problems when we care. The more people know about our incredible marine life and have the opportunity to come face to face with it, the better we will do at making sure our rock pools remain full of mystery and excitement for future generations to discover.

The world has changed since my childhood, but the pools of Porth Mear still hold the same magic now that life has drawn me back. I am no longer alone here, although the beach is still as solitary as ever, shrugging off the outside world with its high-cliffed shoulders. My son and partner sit beside me on the broken-slate shingle, gazing at the foaming edge of the sea, caught up in eating their sandwiches after a day of rock pooling, lost to their thoughts.

Somehow, the life that Ed and I imagined for ourselves before we moved back to the coast has come about. Whether that is through our own decisions or through the gravitational pull of home is hard to tell. I have a habit of following whatever catches my attention, a habit that serves me well in the rock pools, and that I apply to much of my decision making. Through instinct, all the paths I have taken have led back to this coastal life, and I have found myself slipping easily into sharing my discoveries on my Cornish Rock Pools blog, volunteering with local marine groups and turning the beach into a classroom of infinite variety for my Junior and his friends. My journey through the rock pools has taken me around the UK and far beyond, but after all my time away, this beach, unique as all beaches are, feels more familiar than ever.

The deep pools, the flashes of movement and the mystery of what lies under every stone still fill me with wonder, but now I am not the only one kneeling at the edge of the pool staring in. Despite his occasional protests that he's seen it all already, it is rare for my son to miss out on a trip to the beach, and he usually has a list of his own investigations he hopes to do. Whether it's for a family walk or a week-long survey, so we explore and learn together, seeing more by sharing. Off the beach, the internet enables us to connect with others around the county, country and world who are doing similar things and share alike in their discoveries.

We are not the only ones sprawled on the upper shore, eating our picnics today. A group of children and their families from our local Wildlife Watch group have joined us here, many of them already knowledgeable and all of them keen. Linking up with groups of marine recorders, wildlife enthusiasts or litter pickers is a regular occurrence for us now. A movement is growing just when we need it most. The more I experience the power of our shared enthusiasm, knowledge and determination, the more I am assured that there is hope for our wildlife and for our own future, however great the challenges.

For now, we prop ourselves back on our elbows, exhausted from climbing slippery rocks and crawling under overhangs, watching the waves surge in to reclaim what is theirs and breathing the gorse-honeyed air. The cormorants and shags fly up from the distant rocks, followed by oystercatchers as the tide advances, creeping towards us, but our eyes rest on the pools, as though seeing them still, long after they are submerged.

Taking it Further

If you are interested in learning more about rock pooling and coastal wildlife, the following organisations and websites are a great place to start. There may already be a local group that is working to promote marine conservation at your nearest beach, or perhaps you will be the one to set a group up. Your local Wildlife Trust or similar organisations in your area will be pleased to tell you more about their work, local volunteering opportunities and citizen science projects.

Beaches are wonderful places to visit, but always make sure that you check the tide times and do your rock pooling on an outgoing tide, staying away from any dangerous swell. Sturdy boots or shoes are a must to stay safe on the rocks, as is good sun protection and weatherproof clothing. Never harm or remove any animals or seaweed, and if you gently lift rocks be sure to return them exactly how you found them. Traditional rock pooling nets can harm soft-bodied rock pool creatures and crabs' legs are easily tangled in them, so use a bucket or small tub full of seawater to scoop up any animals you would like to observe before returning them where you found them. Remember that the very best way to watch rock pool animals is to sit quietly and watch closely. Joining an organised rock pooling event with local experts will allow you to learn how to rock pool safely and to see far more than you might on your own.

Websites

Aphotomarine: http://www.aphotomarine.com/
Blue Planet Society: http://blueplanetsociety.org/
Capturing Our Coast: https://www.capturingourcoast.co.uk/
Coastwise North Devon: http://www.coastwisenorthdevon.org.uk/
Clean Coasts (Ireland): http://cleancoasts.org/
Community Seagrass Initiative (South West England):
    http://www.csi-seagrass.co.uk/
Cornish Rock Pools: https://cornishrockpools.com/
Field Studies Council: https://www.field-studies-council.org/
Great Eggcase Hunt: https://www.sharktrust.org/en/
    great_eggcase_hunt
iSpot: https://www.ispotnature.org/
Jersey Marine Conservation:
    https://jerseymarineconservation.org.je/
Marine Biological Association: https://www.mba.ac.uk/
Marine Conservation Society: https://www.mcsuk.org/
MarLIN: The Marine Life Information Network:
    https://www.marlin.ac.uk/
Plastic Oceans: http://plasticoceans.uk/
Porcupine Marine Natural History Society: http://pmnhs.co.uk/
Seasearch: http://www.seasearch.org.uk/
Sea Watch Foundation: http://www.seawatchfoundation.org.uk/
Seaquest South West:
    https://www.cornwallwildlifetrust.org.uk/seaquest
Surfers against Sewage: https://www.sas.org.uk/
The Irish Wildlife Trust: https://iwt.ie/
The Scottish Association for Marine Science:
    https://www.sams.ac.uk/
The Seahorse Trust: https://www.theseahorsetrust.org/

The Your Shore Network of Marine Conservation Groups (Cornwall): https://www.cornwallwildlifetrust.org.uk/yourshorenetwork

The Shark Trust: https://www.sharktrust.org/

The Wildlife Trusts (For details of volunteering opportunities, see your local Wildlife Trust's website): https://www.wildlifetrusts.org/

Your Shore Beach Rangers (Cornwall youth opportunities): www.beachrangers.com

Books

A Student's Guide to the Seashore by J.D. Fish and S. Fish (Cambridge University Press, 2011)

Barnacles by A.J. Southward (Published for The Linnean Society and The Estuarine Coast Society by the Field Studies Council, 2008)

British Sea Fishes by Dr Frances Dipper (Underwater World Publications, 2001)

Diver's Guide to Marine Life of Britain and Ireland by Chris Wood (Wild Nature Press, 2018)

Great British Marine Animals by Paul Naylor (Sound Diving Publications, 2011)

Exploring Britain's Hidden World by Keith Hiscock (Wild Nature Press, 2018)

Handbook of the Marine Fauna of North-West Europe by Peter J. Hayward and John S. Ryland (Oxford University Press, 2017)

In the Company of Seahorses by Steve Trewhella and Julie Hatcher (Wild Nature Press, 2017)

Protecting Lundy's Marine Life: 40 Years of Science and Conservation by Keith Hiscock and Robert Irving (Lundy Field Society, 2012)

RSPB Handbook of the Seashore by Maya Plass (Bloomsbury, 2013)

Seasearch Guide to Sea Anemones and Corals of Britain and Ireland by Chris Wood (Wild Nature Press, 2013)

Sea Squirts and Sponges of Britain and Ireland by Sarah Bowen, Claire Goodwin, David Kipling and Bernard Picton (Wild Nature Press, 2018)

Sea Journal by Lisa Woollett (Zart Books, 2016)

Sea Shore of Britain and Europe by Peter Hayward, Tony Nelson-Smith and Chris Shields (Collins, 1996)

Seaweeds of Britain and Ireland by Francis StP. D. Bunker, Juliet A. Brodie, Christine A. Maggs and Anne R. Bunker (Wild Nature Press, 2010)

The Biology of Rocky Shores by Colin Little, Gray A. Williams and Cynthia D. Trowbridge (Oxford University Press, 1998)

The Essential Guide to Beachcombing and the Strandline by Steve Trewhella and Julie Hatcher (Wild Nature Press, 2015)

The Essential Guide to Rock Pooling by Julie Hatcher and Steve Trewhella (Wild Nature Press, 2019)

Index

Acknowledgements

Heartfelt thanks to all those who have encouraged me to write this book and supported me along the way, especially all the fabulous team at September Publishing. I am enormously grateful to Ed and Junior for all those hours on windswept beaches, to my parents for putting up with trays of animals on their dining table, to my friends who have tried to keep me sane and to all the wonderful people who have joined me in my rock pooling adventures. I have been touched by the willingness and thoroughness of all those who have read my work and improved it greatly through their advice and knowledge including: Dr Keith Hiscock, Dr Gordon Watson, Paula Ferris, Cat Gordon, Rob Durrant, Paul Naylor, Matt Slater, Lynne Pope, Jan Whittington, Steve Trewhella, Julie Hatcher, Ed Hagger, Louis Hagger and Derek Buttivant. A big shout out to all the amazing marine groups and volunteers out there. Thank you for everything you do and for letting me be a part of it.